JAMES WITH A SILENT C

Kerry McPhail

© 2011 Kerry McPhail

Published by Linen Press, Edinburgh 2011
1 Newton Farm Cottages
Miller Hill
Dalkeith
Midlothian
EH22 1SA

Email: lynnmichell0@googlemail.com
Website: www.linenpressbooks.co.uk
Blog: linenpressbooks.wordpress.com

ISBN: 978-0-9559618-7-8
Cover photographs: Kerry McPhail and Mr John Hards
Cover design: Submarine, Edinburgh

JAMES WITH A SILENT C

Kerry McPhail

PREFACE

Professor William Rosenberg, Peter Scheuer Chair in Liver Diseases,
Joint Director of the Centre for Hepatology,
University College London, Division of Medicine

James McPhail was a strikingly handsome man with great presence. Being Glaswegian lent both gravity and humour to his words. Intelligent and articulate, he was willing to share the wealth and breadth of his experience to help others, but remained reticent about much of the story recorded in this book. I knew Jim as a softly spoken man with great strength and charm. Smart and respectable in appearance, he was in many ways a typical hepatitis C patient, with only his swollen veined hands hinting at his history of drug use.

Hepatitis C had begun its silent onslaught in Jim's life decades before I met him and was only now making its presence known. Jim bore his illness with great dignity. He displayed immense courage and strength of character despite the setbacks and complications he endured. It was always a pleasure to see him; there was something special about him. His dignity and strength showed no signs of the harshness of his childhood or his chaotic adolescence. Kerry accompanied him on most occasions when we met and the strength of their bond was obvious to all. When Jim's illness worsened, it was evident he derived great strength from Kerry's love and support.

In *James With A Silent C*, Kerry has captured a remarkable story. The terrible sadness of Jim's childhood and the destructive nature of his addiction contrast with the joy of his recovery and their subsequent great love affair. Kerry's book represents a breath-taking account of Jim's path into addiction, the tragedy of his life as an addict and his subsequent recovery and redemption. Kerry's own idyllic childhood is woven into the account of Jim's life until the two are brought together by their love of writing.

This is a very moving story, beautifully told. It was an honour to know Jim. Kerry has written an astonishing story that stands as a fitting tribute to a remarkable man and the woman he loved.

About Hepatitis C

Kerry McPhail

My husband Jim was diagnosed with hepatitis C in 1996 although he had had the disease for many years. After a long battle with deteriorating health, Jim finally made it on to the liver transplant list on 24 September 2007. Desperately ill, he died on 4th December 2007, before a donor organ became available.

Days before his death, Jim reached out to me from his hospital bed, threw his arms around me and told me always to remember how much he loved me.

Hepatitis C is a virus that is carried in the blood and which infects and damages the liver. For people with chronic (long term) hepatitis C, this can eventually lead to cirrhosis, with one in three people developing serious liver disease within twenty to thirty years. It is known as the silent killer because it often goes undetected in its early stages. Hepatitis C is spread by contact with infected blood, for example from open wounds, cuts or scratches. People most at risk are those who inject drugs and people who have received blood transfusions or blood products in the UK before September 1991. Social contact with others who have hepatitis C poses no danger.

In the UK, more than 400,000 people are infected and across the world, 170 million people have hepatitis C. Common symptoms of hepatitis C include fatigue, anxiety, weight loss, intolerance of alcohol, nausea, discomfort around the liver, flu-like symptoms and jaundice.

This book, the story of Jim's life, is a tribute to the man I loved more than life itself. He fought so bravely to survive against the odds. I hope that in telling his story I can publicise the vital importance of the early diagnosis and treatment of hepatitis C.

If detected early on, lives can be saved. Left untreated, many lives will be lost to an entirely preventable liver disease.

All author proceeds from this book are being donated to the British Liver Trust, in Jim's memory.

Thank you.

Kerry

Kerry McPhail

For more information on Hepatitis C and liver diseases, please visit:

The British Liver Trust
www.britishlivertrust.org.uk
and
The Hepatitis C Trust
www.hepctrust.org.uk

ACKNOWLEDGEMENTS

So many wonderful people helped Jim throughout the course of his life. I will never forget your kindness.

To all at Alpha House – you were courageous enough to challenge Jim to turn his life around. Thanks to your support, he succeeded admirably and went on to become a wonderful husband!

I would like also to express my heartfelt thanks to Professor William Rosenberg and his team and to all at the British Liver Trust for all your care and support during Jim's long illness. Where there is great love, there are always miracles and your dedication is proof of this.

To the emergency teams at Queen Alexandra and Southampton General hospitals, I stand in awe of the amazing work you tirelessly perform day in, day out.

To the Transplant Team at Addenbrooke's Hospital in Cambridge, your commitment, courage and integrity are inspirational.

For Beth, Hugh and Kay, may your brother's love remain with you always.

To my father, all our family and friends and in memory of my dear mother, without whom I would not have arrived at the point of writing this book, my heartfelt thanks to you all.

To my amazing friend Heather, whose faith and courage are nothing short of inspirational – I am greatly looking forward to reading your book next!

To my Chief Readers, Heather, Viv, Maureen, Julia, Julie and the two Kays, I am truly grateful to you all for your faith and support. Thanks too to Rob and Chris Richardson at Write-Invite for all your kind encouragement. To all at DWP, thank you for your kindness and support over the years.

Thank you so much to Charles Gore and all at The Hepatitis C Trust for your time, care and support, which is greatly appreciated .

To my publisher, Lynn Michell of Linen Press, thank you so

much for believing wholeheartedly in this book. Your kindness and sensitivity right from the start of this project gave me all the assurance I ever needed that my manuscript could not have been in better hands. Thank you too to Nicky Regan for her exceptional cover design.

Finally, and most importantly, this book is for my dear soul mate Jim – you showed me the true meaning of courage and faith, but above all, you taught me what it really means to love.

PROLOGUE

"Trust you!" I smile, stroking Jim's still warm forehead. "For weeks I've been trying to get you to have an early night and now look at you!"

The clock on the wall says 10 p.m. exactly. I squeeze his hand gently and slip quietly from the room, aware that other patients are asleep nearby.

"Excuse me," I motion to the male duty nurse at the desk.

He turns to face me, enquiringly.

"I think my husband has just passed away."

He is visibly shocked.

"Oh, it's all right," I reassure him. "We've been expecting it."

We? I said 'we'. Did I mean the nurses and I? Rather, I realise, I meant Jim and I. *Team McPhail*, undefeated in sixteen years of battling liver disease. Only this is strange new territory – for both of us.

I nearly lost Jim two years before, in the emergency room. I stayed by his bedside for weeks, watching, waiting and hoping he would make it. He revived, thank God, but this...

Yet I know something now that I had only ever guessed at before. There is a reason for my remarkable calmness. I have experienced a strange kind of wonder that does not readily translate into words. I know instinctively that if I speak of it now, it will be instantly diminished by those gods of the human mind – reason and logic.

So I say nothing.

I am back in the room and another nurse appears. She sits quietly with Jim and me, talking gently to us both, though one of us is no longer listening. My father is on his way. My world has just smashed into a million pieces, yet here I sit, in utter shock, believing it to be intact.

Out in the corridor I can breathe again. It is as if I have been struggling at high altitude and have only now returned to lower ground. Julie, the nurse who cared for Jim in his final hours has already finished her shift. She catches hold of my arm, her eyes full of concern.

"How is he doing?"

"He's just died," I say. Quietly. Simply.

"Oh no! I'm so sorry." She reaches over and hugs me.

"But it was so beautiful, really peaceful." I stare senselessly at her, barely able to comprehend my own reaction.

She too is mystified, yet kind enough to understand that this is where I am at the moment.

I am a ghost now, as I drift silently out of the hospital. It has been raining again – gentle, misty rain – not the dark downpour of the last cruel days. A soft blanket of mist pervades the grounds. Grief too wraps you up in a protective cloak at first. An intense clarity floods your perception in the immediate aftermath of a loved one's death. It lasts at best for a night. Shock follows in its wake, sealing off the entrance to your senses, lest you lose your mind to pain. But it has none of the beauty or majesty of those first precious moments. It is as if time itself steps gallantly aside, retreating, head bowed, to a respectful distance in honour of the departed.

My father is here now. We sit at Jim's side.

"He looks so peaceful, bless him. Good night, Jim. I'm so glad you were part of this family and always will be."

My father speaks to the dead with the easy familiarity of the Irish – raised on a tradition of wakes, long accustomed to farewells. My eyes prick with tears, but none will come yet. I hug Jim until the chill begins to settle on his skin. He appears content, happy even, as if, at the very moment of his departure, he suddenly understood what it had all been about.

"Good night, sweetheart," I whisper, kissing his dear forehead. I can still hear his voice in my head, sing-songing those very words to me across the bed at home. Only now there is an aching chasm between us that can never be filled.

Home alone, I am forever awake. The late night Shipping Forecast and I are intimately acquainted. Listening to the theme tune *Sailing By* has become my strategy for survival, my indication that I am still clawing my way back to sanity.

Strange, the odyssey grief sets you on. Rather like sailors in ancient times, who feared they would sail off the edge of the world if they ventured too far, I drift great distances from the moorings of real life. I wonder if the future horizon holds only terror? Mythical monsters rear up from the depths of my tortured imagination. I clutch my stomach, curled up tight in the foetal position, wondering if I will ever be released from the enormity of this pain. Unsteady as a ship, hurled into the eye of a hurricane, I stagger with my efforts to cross the storm-soaked deck of my own existence. All pretence of maintaining the rigging of daily life is gone. I am drenched, exhausted, and desolate. I haven't even the dubious comfort of company on board. I am alone on this voyage.

Somewhere in the darkness, a light reaches in and pierces the very centre of my being, a lone star. Perhaps I only sense it, but it is deep within my soul. I have to trust that it will not let me go. I set my course, using it to steer by. Ancient mariners relied upon such stars. Compasses fail and man is forever at the mercy of the elements. Such men were wise to throw themselves upon God's mercy.

I survive on Temazepam, two a day. I would take more, but the doctor will only prescribe four at a time. I am deeply resentful of this; I cannot sleep at all without them. Later I will realise he knows, better than I do, just how much I am struggling. Finally I begin to see how pain can sometimes be so bad, you will do whatever it takes to get rid of it. I turn to writing, in a desperate bid to stay afloat, and in so doing, I begin to unravel Jim's story...

PART 1

CHAPTER 1
Glasgow 1956

"Have you got the bread?"

"Aye, right here. Don't panic."

Jim scoots his shoes on and peers into the bucket.

"Does Mum know you've got all that?"

"Course she does!"

"Bet she doesn't!" He declares with satisfaction, hopping and jumping around his older sister Beth.

Saturday afternoon on the corner of Oswald and Argyle Street and taxis draw up close, cutting across the tramlines. Jim chats excitedly as Beth grabs his hand and they cross the busy main road together. He wrestles free the minute they touch the kerb. He is a big boy now, nearly five. They are barely two minutes from the railway station and its secluded dark archways are lit up, an Aladdin's cave of golden shop fronts, enticing you in from a backdrop of gloomy rain.

Hugh, the eldest at ten, bears their father's first name. He trails sedately behind. Kay, the baby of the family, is at home with their mother.

St Peter's Church was converted into Wilson's Zoo in the 1930s. A beady eyed mynah bird greets their arrival.

"Pretty boy, how're ye?" He squawks affectionately, eyeing them with detached curiosity.

Mice and tame baby rats inhabit the basement floors in rows of untidy cages. They would fit in your pocket and it's awfully tempting to lift one. Snakes and reptiles move silently about their lairs, tongues darting in and out. They wouldn't survive the dead cold of a Glaswegian winter outside. Down here, among the heat lamps, even they are stultified, desperately in need of the blazing heat of their native lands. Tiny golden finches flit fitfully between the bars of their cages, flashes of jewelled wings, rare as paradise, in the confines of the dusky surroundings.

All three children are totally absorbed, alerting each other to an acrobatic feat or alluring plumage. They kneel reverentially at the porcupine enclosure, peering in expectantly, but the elusive creature cannot be seen at either end of his tunnel. In all their visits to date they have yet to see him emerge.

"Don't reckon he's even in there!" declares Hugh, superciliously.

Jim shuts his eyes tight and wishes hard, certain he will be the first to see him. Beth screws her face up, cynically.

"I reckon they've just put a sign up, saying he's in there, but really it's just an empty cage."

"Me too!" Jim chips in, stoutly. Secretly, his hopes are dashed.

A low growl thunders overhead, causing their insides to tremble. They charge upstairs in a trice. A lion lives here, in a cage barely eighteen feet by eight. Lifting his poor emaciated head, he peers through the bars and eyes the children warily. His mane is untamed and matted. Sensing prey, he lifts his head and sniffs the air, ferocious and battle weary. The children fidget outside his cage, egging one another on to put their faces as near to him as they dare. He sinks down again, heavily, onto his straw bed that stinks of urine and faeces. In his prime, the lion's teeth were removed after he attempted to bite his keeper. Now it costs sixpence to come and see him, unless you bring a bucket of bread, in which case it's free.

The ill-lit confined gloomy space of an old converted church building is no place for the King of the Jungle to rest his head. For all the ancient prayers that hang heavily in the air, the old lion is forced to dream of the lost African plains of his ancestors. Born into captivity, sleep is his only escape from the reality that has killed him long before death will arrive.

Flitting like butterflies, they rush from one exhibited animal to the next, thrilled by the panther, chuckling at the squabbling monkeys, wary of the vicious bites of the ferrets. On their way out, they see the mynah bird still arguing with his reflection in a mirror.

Long after the children's laughter has reverberated around the walls, the old lion, ancient and regal, brought low by humankind, stares depressively through the bars of his cage. A bluebottle fizzes distractedly at his bars, tormenting him with its show of freedom.

Jim jumps and runs along the road home, grabbing Beth's hand one minute, diving free the next; wanting her and not wanting her, hell-bent on exploring the ruined building opposite their home. A huge wall on Robertson Street conceals a derelict wasteland of weeds; sometimes he slips through a gap in the wall to play there amid the rubble.

Later, Jim's head sinks down onto his pillow. He stares out into the darkness. His brother Hugh is in the room now. He can just make out his shadow on the wall opposite. Everywhere around them lie books and records, abandoned shoes and clothes. A game of Ludo, contents scattered on the floor, half finished. Each blames the other for the mess. He thinks of his mother and father in the next room, enjoying a cup of tea. His father smoking his pipe, his mother lost in crocheting a blanket. Satisfied that all is well with the world, he closes his eyes and goes to sleep.

Round the corner, the lion shifts uncomfortably on the concrete floor of his cage and causes the other animals to stir warily in the dark. Turning around and around, he sinks back into fitful sleep. Only in dreams does he escape the torment of his existence.

Jim's father pauses, taking in the night air, before closing the door and locking up for the night. King of the household, perhaps sensing, with a primal instinct, that his own days are drawing to a close. The rational part of him, that excludes such supernatural proclivities, shrugs it off, dismissing it as melancholy. He goes indoors to join his family, asleep in the sanctity of home.

CHAPTER 2

There are only a few snapshots, tucked away in the back of the sideboard. Margaret found them while she was having a bit of a sort out, but today is not the time to look at them. She is too preoccupied. She can't manage even a side-sweeping glance of astonishment at her good fortune.

He is a beautiful child. Big, thoughtful eyes, chubby cheeks, rosebud mouth and his button of a nose set perfectly in their midst. What an old soul her youngest lad is already; busy concentrating on the butterflies that flit in and out of the backyard at her mother's house in Possil. There has never been a child like him, before or since. Nor will there be. He belongs to Margaret alone, but she does not realise what a precious gift he is.

Here he is again, a little boy of five. Hair neatly swept over the right side of his forehead. Here and there, spikes of fringe have rebelled, sticking defiantly upward. He is poised beside a sandcastle on the beach at Barmouth. His daddy took that shot. She remembers it well. Jim's face is lit up with excitement, his hands spread out proudly, displaying his achievement.

Look at them all in this one! Sitting in a row inside a caravan, the following year: Margaret, Jim, Beth and Kay, smiling into Hugh's devoted lens. Light from the window streams in behind them, illuminating Jim's dear face. Margaret herself looks troubled, she realises now. An aloof mother hen, she should have had her arm around them, instead of which they are perched stiffly alongside her. Jim is beaming, already lost in a narrative of his own; dreaming of the seaside, perhaps. The caravan is bare except for a shelf overhead. The minute the shutter clicked, they must have let out a collective sigh of relief and spilled outwards, arms and legs in all directions like an expanding Alice in Wonderland outgrowing the walls of her house.

Margaret sees only her husband, Hugh, in these photos, even though he does not appear in a single one of them, being forever behind the camera. She shoves them back into the envelope, putting them in among his paperwork and bills. She can't face them at the moment. Pursing her lips, she glances at the clock.

Jim throws himself through the front door, satchel bumping against the wall.

"I'm first back, Mum!" He announces cheerily, out of breath, having run all the way.

She chides him, but he is exuberant still.

"Guess what?" He demands, "Guess what I did today?"

But Margaret is not in the mood for guessing.

Jim gives up. He can't get her to pay him what he's owed. She seems oblivious to the debt of love she's taken on. He's doing his best, but he can't get by on the meagre portion she doles out to him. He's only seven. He needs more. He tries to get her to understand, demanding she stop and listen to his day, insistently tugging at her sleeve, while she peels potatoes. But she is permanently distracted. She gets cross. Can't he see she's busy?

He helps himself, eventually; only a penny or two at first, from her purse, left open on the table.

This is how bad it is; she doesn't even notice. He slinks away, deeply ashamed. He spends it on sweeties and gives half of them away. He doesn't want them really. Even gnawing on his ill-gotten toffee only serves to remind him how terribly hungry he really is.

He stops as soon as he is found out. Bitterly disappointed in himself, imagining a terrible stain on his character, he is not surprised that his mother doesn't love him. He's no good underneath, is he? He's just proved it to himself.

Of course Margaret is aware that Jim is struggling but it's all part of growing up, she reasons to herself. Didn't she too struggle once?

Why can't he just enjoy himself like the other wee lads around here? Take the Burns' boys over there, playing with a red balloon on a string. Other people's children seem so much less demanding than her own, she considers wearily.

*

"Mum, it's my birthday soon, isn't it?" Jim demands, excitedly, skipping down the road beside her.

Kay, his sister, is in her pushchair and leans out, grinning toothily at him.

"When is it, Mum? It's soon, isn't it?"

Margaret swallows. She contemplates a white lie, but God might be listening.

"It was yesterday, son."

She feels terrible, of course. The little face, brightly optimistic in spite of everything, unravels in front of her. She bends down to button up his jersey.

"Never mind, ma wee pet lamb. We'll make up for it somehow, eh?"

The pushchair wheels rattle on, over Jim's dreams, and on up towards Argyle Street.

*

"Mum, is there a God?"

Jim swirls a finger round the mixing bowl his mother has deposited on the kitchen table. A late birthday cake. Margaret says she can't make his mind up for him. Jim himself must decide for himself. Jim considers the matter long and hard, swinging his legs from his chair as he does so.

"If there is a God, why wouldn't He want to make Daddy better?"

He reasons.

Margaret has no answer for that one. God's ways are not her ways, she thinks, grimly. She wishes he was like the others and went out a bit more. Instead he clutters the flat up – always reading – head forever buried in a comic. He seems content just sitting there in the quiet, knowing his dad is in the next room. Poor Hugh, he is so worn out now, thinks Margaret. The doctors have yet to pronounce their final verdict. She hasn't told the children yet. She knows she will have to. Sooner or later the choice will be swept from under her, but until then, there's no point in them all suffering. Bad enough having to gaze into Hugh's eyes, his face etched delicately with concern for her, as she tries to convince him it is all going to be all right. She can handle this, can't she? God wouldn't really let her down, would He?

People don't understand. They don't realise that cancer isn't a disease you can catch, like measles or TB.

Hugh appears in the doorway and calls out in distress. "Help me, Margaret, I can't cope with the pain!" He clutches his abdomen with a wafer thin hand.

Jim stares bleakly up at him then instantly returns his gaze to his comic. But the images have scorched his retina, burning into places where tears would not dare surface. Jim doesn't believe in God, he decides emphatically. He shuts his comic and slips on his shoes and coat, stepping quietly outside the front door, taking care not to slam it loudly. Once in the street, he begins to run, cautiously at first, then gathering speed as he races down towards the Clyde. Whatever it is inside him, he yearns to outrun it so that he never has to feel it again. The wind whips his cheeks, burning his skin, and his coat flaps wildly open on either side, like a cape. He is possessed of super powers. God might not be able to save his daddy in time, but Batman can…

Chapter 3

It's the same dream, over and over. Margaret is stepping towards the edge of a cliff. Any second now, she will lose her footing and God alone knows what will happen to her then.

She wakes in a rush, heart racing, catching her breath. Hugh is still asleep beside her. His shoulder shudders briefly. He's exhausted, but on some level he has been stirred by her need of him. Oh and Margaret does have need of him! She might brazen it out, tough as a soldier, but the army can only march for so long on limited rations. The doctors do not hold out much hope for him now. Treatment is restricted to whatever will alleviate the pain.

In the next room, Jim is fast asleep. Oblivion is the best pain killer of all. In his dreams, his father is a picture of health, sitting astride his motorbike. Jim is perched behind him, arms wrapped tightly around his waist as they race along, down by the Clyde, not far from Jamaica Bridge. High up, you see the world from a different perspective. In dreams at least, the pair are invincible.

"Are you up yet?" Margaret calls.

He never is. Jim clings tenaciously to his dreams. She could do without the morning rush, with four children and an incapacitated husband to look after. But then Hugh's no trouble at all, she reminds herself. He rarely stirs these days.

Up the road they troop reluctantly. What do the teachers expect of them? We're not talking about hot housing here and besides, orchids do not spring forth from this kind of soil. These kids are dirt rough, mere weeds pushing up between stone and bricks because that's all that Anderston has to offer them. Concrete and poverty. No hope. No shot at redemption. It's just as well that most of them aren't wasting their time searching for it.

The teachers can't have it both ways. You can't bury a pupil's dreams and expect him to thrive.

"You've never had it so good," declares Harold McMillan, as his government waggles an accusing finger at the public by way of the media. Did Harold ever show his face in Anderston?

Look at the poor little runts, queuing up in the shower blocks once a week on a Friday after school, clutching their threadbare towels under their arms because not one of them has a bathroom at home. It's a stand-up wash by the sink all week. This is their one chance to rid themselves of the perpetual itch of grime that settles on their skin in this smog-ridden city. No doubt they don't smell too good come the end of the week, but what can they do? Good job they're all in the same boat, really. That way, no one notices.

Jim is self conscious at first, until he spots wee Barry. He lost his left leg in an accident and has a wooden prosthetic limb. Jim watches in horrified fascination as Barry calmly removes it, props it up against the wall and hobbles into the shower. You just have to get on with it, he realises, shivering in the draught. No choice.

"You lot are fit for the factory or the Big House, don't ever expect to amount to anything!" On and on bellows the teacher, like a stuck gramophone record, strap in hand, defying anyone to disagree with him.

Jim casts his eye out of the window with its view of grey derelict buildings on all sides. He thinks of his father, at home in bed, blending seamlessly into his surroundings as his cancer progresses. His father, whose body, like the condemned buildings, is unfit for human habitation. His daddy who once worked on the railways and called him Shamus because it is Gaelic for James. His daddy, who never worked in a factory, who never got sent to the Big House. Jim is better than this, whatever the teachers say. He's worth more than they think. He knows it. He'll show them. He'd better do. He's got a vested interest in getting out of here.

At playtime, a boy takes a knife out and calmly carves into the back of another lad's shirt. What can the teachers hope to achieve here? This is 1950s Glasgow, not Strangeways, though thankfully, Ofsted isn't around yet to point out the essential difference. Certainly they could do with riot control training at Woodside Primary.

"Ye've got great tits, miss!" Pipes up a ten year old in Jim's class. "I'd like tae get ma hons on 'em!"

In and out the revolving door they go. Caned, chastised, returned, unbridled. It's water dripping fresh off a duck's back.

Jim keeps his head down.

"If only you all worked as hard as Jim McPhail here does!" Remonstrates the teacher. Jim lets out a huge sigh. He could do without it, he really could.

Two new lads arrive, immigrants from Canada. They are duly lined up at the makeshift goal posts on the concrete outside.

"Celtic or Rangers?"

"Eh?"

"Which do you support, Celtic or Rangers?"

They freeze. Nine years old and not from round here, they are faced now with fifty enquiring faces, horridly aware that their answers matter deeply.

"Better get it right!" Their sharp-faced perpetrator warns.

"Celtic?" A wild stab in the dark in the absence of any clues.

"Wrong answer!"

Twenty pairs of hands descend on them and tie them to the goal posts. They are screaming in fright as they are lashed again and again with ropes. Nobody comes near. The teachers are apparently oblivious to what is going on right in front of their eyes.

Jim is sickened to the stomach by what he has seen. He walks home alone.

"Oi! Jimbucket! Coming to the bridge?" Five of the boys push past him. He shakes his head as they run off, the feeling of abandonment in him battling with revulsion at the thought of even wanting to fit in. Raymond gets it. He would. He's the only Pakistani in the entire school. Boy, does Raymond ever get it!

"Glad we can hang out together, eh?" Raymond passes him. They stop and chat briefly. Raymond lives too far away for friendship to flourish outside of school. In any case, it is not long before he too is bowing to peer pressure, desperate to be accepted, not to suffer anymore.

Jim studies furiously now, determined he will move up and away from them all. He makes it to the top of his year and wins a little prize. A book. He is glowing inwardly. Rushing home, he shows his father. Hugh smiles gently at his son, who privately notes the exhaustion on his father's face as he leafs through the book with admiration.

If only Hugh could appreciate how much Jim needs him right now. But Hugh needs more than Jim. Hugh needs a miracle. These, he concludes, are pretty thin on the ground in Anderston.

He endures the regime as best he can, drawing stoically on his pipe. It won't do any good giving it up now. He clings to Margaret for support. She helps him in and out of the bathroom. The children are anxious to keep the noise down. It is too small a flat to contain them all, but they try their best.

Hugh wanted a garden. He misses the wild expanse of his native Highlands. Margaret would have liked that too, a few roses blooming out the back. Instead there are only weeds, forcing their way up uninvited through the gaps in the concrete. Like the rats that thrive in the old brickwork factory close by, they are forever on the increase.

Jim goes to bed, clutching his little book. It is a symbol of hope. It is all he has. He closes his eyes and dreams of a future far from Woodside Primary. It's for the best, then, that he doesn't see too far ahead. Not just yet.

Later, his brother stumbles into bed, glowing from a date with his girlfriend. He watches his younger brother whose face smiles seamlessly in his dreams. Gently he removes the book from his arms and places it on the bedside table.

Margaret reaches out across the bedclothes and clutches Hugh's hand. Neither of them speak about it. It is too painful to contemplate. He gathers her fingers, warm and safe in his own, in answer to her unspoken query. She closes her eyes, memorising the sensation of his touch. Trying not to think of a time when he will no longer be there to comfort her.

Chapter 4

Father Christmas has been in the night, but he has neglected to bring the one thing the McPhail family needed – a miracle. There weren't any to be had in the shops come closing time on Christmas Eve where Margaret battled through the late night crowds until, defeated, she made her way to their new home.

Now it is Christmas morning and it is snowing outside. All around is the gentle, sacred silence of dawn. Margaret steps outside the door of their new home on West Princes Street and stands there for a moment, marvelling at the peace. No one is about at this hour. She huddles her dressing gown tight around her. Each of these snowflakes is unique but they melt the instant they touch the pavement and merge into the damp. They are all the same. Is this the only difference between this life and the next, she wonders? Each beautiful individuality, so essential in the living human form, is rendered utterly inconsequential by death.

Even Hugh is no longer himself. Cancer is dissembling him, bit by bit, devouring his muscles, drawing hollows around his eyes and concave cheeks. He smiles at her as she enters the bedroom, motioning delicately for her to sit by him. Taking her cold hand in his, he warms her heart. She is startled by this intimacy. The sheer beauty of his focus being anywhere other than on his own suffering touches her deeply. Perhaps the greatest gift of all is the ability to love so dearly, even in the face of one's own decline. Why, like all the best gifts, is it saved until last?

The children are up. They hover in the doorway before running in to kiss their dad on the cheek. Then it's off to attend to the few wee parcels under the tree in the living room. They start on the chocolate for breakfast. Jim spots a Fry's Five Boys bar in his stocking; five lads' faces peer out from the wrapper, each countenance expressing a different emotion. He instinctively feels sorry for the crying boy, and, ripping off the wrapper, he bites decisively into a piece. Next he unwraps a Topper annual and turns the pages.

Last night, listening in the dark, they half expected sleigh bells. Now even Kay no longer believes Father Christmas can step in and save the day.

Jim takes his dad a hot cup of tea. Perched on the end of the bed, he is troubled by how weak his father looks.

"You all right, son? Happy Christmas!" His father beams, ruffling his son's hair.

Jim shrugs, embarrassed, yet secretly enjoying this show of affection. His mind is turning somersaults. He rushes over to the window.

"Look, Dad! It's been snowing!"

"That right, son?" Hugh eyes the flurry of flakes, nodding in confirmation as if noticing them for the first time.

Hugh is helped into his dressing gown and slippers and pads gently out into the living room on Margaret's arm. Beth rushes up to put cushions in his armchair and help her mother settle him down.

Nobody alludes to the fact it is the last time.

Everybody knows that it is.

Whatever must it be like for Hugh? He gazes longingly at them all, knowing he has a long journey ahead of him.

The ambulance men are on their way. Hugh manages a couple of spoonfuls of Christmas dinner – a piece of turkey and a sprout, just to please Margaret. Her big, proud husband, skeletal now, with his pipe in hand; a badly drawn stick man in a huge armchair.

In the kitchen, amid the steaming saucepans and the sink piled high with washing up, Margaret takes a sip of sherry. The dry sting burns the back of her throat, reassuring her that she is still alive and functioning in this nightmare.

Her mother and father descend and settle around the children.

The lights are still twinkling in the window as they drive Hugh away to hospital. Margaret goes with him, while Granny stays with the children. In George Square, the huge decorated tree bears up against the stark cold sky. A star on its topmost branch beckons them towards the General Hospital.

Not long now. It would be best to say all the things that matter most rather than leaving it too late but the words stick in Margaret's throat. The best she can do is to express her love in the prim little kisses she leaves on Hugh's forehead and in the way she turns round to look at him every time she leaves the ward – reluctantly in case it is the last time. She is privately committing him to her memory.

Jim is at his daddy's side now, devastated to see how he is wasting away. He looks like the prisoners of war he has seen in films at the cinema. His ribs stick out either side of his body. Hollow-cheeked, bare headed, like a man awaiting execution. No pipe for him now.

"Be a good lad for your mum, Shamus!" His father whispers to his youngest son. The words barely drift off his lips before he sinks back onto the pillows. The effort has cost him too much.

Hugh doesn't live to see another spring. Long before the thaw arrives, he slips silently away.

Margaret, whey faced, is back from the hospital, frozen to the bone. She sinks down onto her chair in the kitchen and gathers her children to her. This is the hardest task she has ever had to undertake in her entire life.

"I'm so sorry. Your daddy has died."

They are astounded at this – the news they were all secretly dreading.

Jim bursts into tears. Racing to his room, he throws himself onto his bed, howling into his pillows. His poor daddy, gone! He didn't even tell him how much he loved him! He is tormented by the fact that he will never know.

He listens out for his mother. Surely she will come to him and comfort him? He needs her so very much right now. Where is she? She can't leave him all alone, feeling like this, with a pain in his tummy! But his mother doesn't come. Exhausted, Jim falls asleep at last, fully clothed on top of his blankets.

It grows dark. Margaret is still sitting in the kitchen, transfixed, cup in hand, staring into the distance.

*

"He was a good man, Margaret."

"He didnae deserve tae die young like that, leaving a wee family behind and all…"

"You take good care of yourself, hen. If there's anything you need – anything at all – you just call."

The voices in her head fade into the distance as the railway men depart. All of Hugh's former friends and colleagues came to pay their respects. Margaret is deeply touched by their kindness.

Her children did her proud, scrubbed to within an inch of their lives, their hair plastered neatly back, the boys in suits, Beth and Kay in their best dresses. Each of them eyeing her from time to time in the pew, making sure she is coping. Afterwards, there is the tender shock of her eldest son's hand on hers at the meal. She draws hers away so quickly because tears are threatening to engulf her. She wants to cling on to her dignity.

You've got to wonder if the Big Man really knows what He's doing. Even Margaret is questioning her faith. Certainly it makes you wonder at the sense of it all. Occasionally she feels Hugh's presence near her, as if he is quietly at her side still, encouraging her to carry on.

*

Spring is an agony best forgotten. When the daffodils raise their trumpet heads in the park, she half expects them to herald his return. How she waits, day after day, by the window at home, aching inside, longing for him to turn the corner and wave in her direction. When the truth finally hits home, it devastates her.

Margaret tries to reconcile herself to the fact that Hugh is no longer suffering. But then, Hugh is no longer here, either. How is that better, exactly? He is with God. But where is God? Wherever is God when you really need him?

For months she fights back the urge to burst into tears. It steals over her like a black cloud, even when she is out in public, threatening to overwhelm her and to drain all the hope from her world.

Margaret is only looking for answers and you can't blame her for that. People don't understand the dark abyss of grief; they assume it gets better over time, but it doesn't. It remains as stark and unacceptable as ever. You just get better at pretending to cope, that's all. Sometimes, to Margaret's horror, it even gets worse. Darker. Deeper. There are times when she wonders if she will ever reconnect to the world around her. Faith does not begin to address the issue. Margaret has become mechanised by grief. In the absence of any outlet for her pain, she has fought to internalise it. She gets pills at first to help her sleep, then she gets on with it. 'Getting on with it' means switching to drink to help her function because the doctors have stopped prescribing medication. It means steeling herself to cope with the bone grinding exhaustion of raising four grieving children alone while remaining the sole breadwinner.

Margaret pushes her nails hard into the palms of hands in her pockets. No one sees. No one really knows what she is going through.

Her patients at the hospital where she works need her and she responds wholeheartedly to them. They don't torture her with memories like everyone else does. Her children, with their haunting mannerisms, remind her desperately of Hugh. Reality is demanding way too much of Margaret.

She looks up wearily at the clock on the mantelpiece at home, hardly able to believe that in two hours time she will have to go through the charade of another whole day.

She decides to make a pot of tea to ease her in and remembers this time to only set one cup instead of the usual two.

Closing her eyes, she recalls how she first set eyes on Hugh all those years ago. Bright, inquisitive, witty and so, so handsome. In the dark, in the silence and safety of solitude, she buries her face in her bedclothes and lets out an agony of tears.

The boy in the bedroom has learnt that it does no good to cry. Nobody sees or hears his pain, so Jim buries it instead. He swallows it down and becomes nervous and edgy, mistrustful of other people. He is distant, dreamy and unreachable, desperately trying to invent a way out of his pain. He tries his hardest to remember happiness. Hugh dreamed of taking them all to live in Australia, once. Now he will never even see them grow up. Where did they all go – all those unfulfilled promises, blown like sand across a beach?

Jim delves into another Marvel comic, with his torch beneath the bedclothes. He devours them. When he snaps the light off, he sees only death stars and holes in the universe that can never be fixed. He and his mother are locked in their own private agony. Each is isolated by the other's boundaries and they cannot comfort each other.

There is a photograph on the mantelpiece of Hugh and Margaret sat side by side in the park. They look relaxed and happy, at ease in the sunshine. They were so in love, the pair of them. It is all that remains of them now.

PART 2

Chapter 5

"You all right there, son? Come in and have a wee cup of tea with us!"

Jim helps out on a milk round now, in the mornings, before school.

He loves it, sitting at someone else's kitchen table where he is made to feel warmly welcome.

That cold northerly has switched directions at last and is blowing in Jim's favour. He's even started getting into trouble at school.

"You! Jim McPhail! Go and sit in the corner!" The teacher booms, exasperated at Jim who is clowning around again in maths.

Jim slouches over to the corner, enjoying the surprised grins on his classmates' faces.

"And you, Ed. Since you appear to find it so funny, perhaps you'd care to join him?"

Fatal mistake on the teacher's part because they hit it off instantly, sharing the same sense of humour and a longing to be part of something. Greg soon joins them too. An instant hit, this trio.

"Watch out – here come The Three Stooges!" Laughs Ed's mother, but she approves of them, just the same.

"You're nothing but a bunch of punks!" The Headmaster shouts in despair when they are called to his room again.

They are too, hanging out at pubs and gigs, underage, gangly and impossibly cool, outraging decent society with their long hair and psychedelic music.

Jim doesn't care. He is fourteen and the world's opinion rarely mattered less to him.

By 1967 they are hippies. It's official. Posing on the high stone gateposts at Kelvingrove Park, they stare moodily into the distance, like a rudimentary Pink Floyd on a photo shoot. Arthur, Paul and Callum soon join their group. Arthur is charismatic, witty and generous to a fault. He and Jim gel instantly. Paul bears an uncanny resemblance to Jim and they are often mistaken for brothers. Jim feels instantly protective towards him, going to great lengths to shield him from the dope scene that he is fast becoming immersed in. Callum, shy and introverted, is a highly talented musician.

Jim can scarcely believe his luck; he has so many friends now. Take Mick and Rusty. He met them on his milk round and now he regularly smokes dope with them at their house. He isn't mad keen on dope, but it does at least reinforce his wish to be different, which, perversely, is exactly what it takes to fit in around here.

In the winter, it is bitterly cold. Jim's hands are raw agony if he forgets to wear his gloves. Look at the veins on the back of his hand – almost blue! It's a slippery pathway, leading to Mick's house; got to watch your step, delivering the milk there. One foot wrong and you could be in trouble...

Does Jim realise the potential peril of falling? The ditch before him is covered in leaves. It doesn't look deep, but it's deceptive – like so many things in life. You can't really see how far down it goes, especially when it's covered in snow.

*

When summer comes, Mick and Rusty leave for England and another Mick steps ably into their place, along with his pal George. They inherit the good will from the hashish business, diversifying into other lines of work as the fancy takes them.

Whoever would have thought that a simple milk round could introduce you to such an eclectic mix of society? Surely the Milk Marketing Board are missing a trick when it comes to advertising their vacancies?

Mick pays Jim in kind for the milk now. The milk, in turn, pays for itself, being stolen. Jim is quick to appreciate the importance of profit margins. In business you reduce costs wherever you can.

Jim is tight-lipped about the whole affair which is just as well. He applies to the Post Office for work and the Medical Examination Board advise his teeth are rotten. If he wants a job, he has to get them fixed first. He's not sure what he wants. His best guess would be happiness, but he can only find dealers in hashish, which leaves him a few consonants short. Rather like solving a cryptic crossword clue, the answer is in there somewhere but it keeps eluding him.

Margaret, at least, is relieved about the job. A bit more money coming in, a bit less going out. But privately she is worried about Jim. Clearly he is smart, but he lacks direction. Her eldest son, Hugh, is already married, having left Glasgow and moved to England. Respectability, that's all that Margaret wants for Jim.

Jim is on his way home from Edinburgh. He's been in digs all week, undertaking his Post Office induction training. Now he has a pressing call to make, so he wends his way round to Frank-the-Hippie's house.

'Dr Frank, self-styled physician to the masses, offers him a prescription for a brighter future – LSD. This is more like it! Strawberry Fields, Purple Haze, White Light. The dream marriage of Jim's twin loves, music and oblivion. He is seventeen, with his whole life ahead of him.

"Go on, man. Try half a tab," Frank urges.

They all want him to do well: Margaret, Frank, the GPO. They all want him to succeed. It's just that they each have a different vision for Jim. Frank's involves hearing the trees grow, listening to what the grass has to say for itself and experiencing how it feels to be inside the mind of God. The Post Office training manual hasn't touched on these topics yet. Today's chapter concentrated on Postal Orders and Premium Bonds and was shockingly down to earth.

Christmas is rolling round again. Jim is all for the bright lights and peace that LSD affords him with its amazing insights and the benefit of flashbacks. It's the gift that goes on giving.

Two weeks later, Jim calls round at Frank's again. But tonight, he does not make it home afterwards.

Expecting Frank's genial welcome, Jim is surprised when Alex answers the door. Alex is a known drug dealer whom Jim has met before with his associate John when they were sitting outside the house with several pounds of black hashish.

"Frank's out, Jim, but come on in." Alex ushers him into the hallway. He is a dark, majestic ringleader, overseeing the macabre circus that is unfolding within.

Alex won't take no for an answer. That's the trouble with tricky customers, Jim reasons. The Post Office would advise listening carefully to their complaint and asking open questions to establish a satisfactory outcome. But Jim is guessing the Post Office have yet to attend one of Alex's parties.

It is very dark in here. None of the usual dopey, hazy ambiance tonight. A feeling of gloom pervades the room.

"A'right, man?" A man with broken teeth raises his head briefly to acknowledge Jim. All around him, figures are conked out on the floorboards, like zombies in a B-movie.

"Come on through, Jim. Got something I want to show you." Alex steps over the prostrate forms and Jim reluctantly follows.

"John!" He nods briefly. For there, sat in the middle of the room, is John, engaged in pharmaceutical research. Bottles of heroin and morphine, tincture of opium, capsules and tablets of barbiturates and speed lie all around him.

What has Jim walked in on? His heart begins pounding. His throat contracts, but he cannot summon up the courage to leave. Alex is a major leader in the Glasgow gang scene and is not a man to risk offending.

"I'm going to give you a bit of H, Jim," Alex announces.

He takes his time, getting it ready; showing Jim each stage, the way a doctor reassures a patient ahead of a procedure. He chops out the smack.

"This is what I'm going to give you." He advises, putting the smack in a syringe. "You're going to enjoy this." He instructs, putting a belt on Jim's arm.

Jim's options are now as restricted as his blood flow. Alex wastes no time in finding a vein, the needle penetrates his arm and the deed is done. There is no going back. The ramifications of this single moment are vast and set to change the course of many lives. But all that lies ahead for now.

Jim is completely overwhelmed which is hardly surprising since he has just taken a massive overdose. His head is throbbing. The room spins violently around him. He lies on the bed, desperately struggling to keep his eyes open. Jim knows that if he shuts them, even for a second, he is gone. No one but no one here would even consider calling an ambulance for him, so he has no choice. He must somehow survive.

An hour passes. Jim fights ferociously, clinging to the walls for support. The room is ricocheting around him. He frantically searches for the toilet, clutching on to the banister in the hall. Everyone is laughing in his face, a carousel of grinning bastards who fly past him on the landing. Only towards dawn does the spinning recede. He throws up, utterly spent. Finally he can stand and walk without hanging on for dear life.

He has to go home. He has to explain to his mother where he has been all night.

Creeping into the flat at last, he breathes out and nearly bursts into tears at the effort it has cost him to get here. He is ready to face Margaret and longs to confide in her that he needs help, but she is asleep in bed. Did she even notice that he was missing?

Somewhere in her exhaustion, Margaret marked the opening of

the front door and the return of her youngest son. She had lain awake until the early hours, waiting for him, but eventually sleep claimed her. She is too afraid of what is happening to confront him.

Jim shivers under his bedclothes. He tries to wrap them tightly around him, longing for a hug. He aches to be a boy again with his father at his side. He hates heroin. That room stank of death. He never wants to come near it again.

CHAPTER 6

"Ye all right there, hen?"

Margaret looks up and smiles. She is ward sister at the Ear, Nose and Throat Hospital now. Her patients are very fond of her. Certainly Davie McKenna is. In fact, he would like to get his feet under her kitchen table but Margaret's going to take some persuading for that to happen. He makes her laugh, right enough; he can see that she needs a tonic. He reckons he's the man for the job.

Typical Jack the Lad is Davie, though of course he tones down his racist remarks when Margaret's listening. He saves his 'darkies, kikes, wops and yids' talk for when his brother comes over from America and they trade stories and play cards. His brother works on a building site.

"Chucked a couple of bricks at a pair of niggers passing under the scaffolding just the other day," he boasts, casually.

"That'll teach the bastards to stay in their own country!" Grins Davie, savagely.

Margaret doesn't know all this, of course. Not yet. He makes her laugh when he is clowning about with her. Dressed in his hospital gown, Davie is a sanitised version of himself, not a nasty racist thug. Will she see through him in time?

Let's not make light of the fact that he makes her laugh – Margaret, who has barely raised a smile since Hugh died and left her alone to raise four children single-handedly.

Davie, with his happy-go-lucky approach to life, has inexplicably pulled Margaret out of the mire but where he plans to set her down again is anyone's guess. He has cancer of the ear. Surgeons performed an operation on the growth and accidentally hit a nerve and as a result, the skin on the left side of his face hangs limply down and his left eye never closes. This is disconcerting since you cannot tell if he is awake or asleep. Davie is partial to sleeping pills, swallowing Nembutal, Tuinal, Mandrax, DF118s, Palfium and Diconal by the handful so it's safe to assume he is usually in the land of nod.

His whole demeanour is that of a shuffling ex-boxer, punch drunk and down on his luck. Bitter at the treatment life has meted out to him, he can sponge drinks from the entire bar at the Saracen's Head. The only wee man in the whole of Glasgow who can go out empty-handed, yet return completely bladdered. Good at spinning a yarn is Davie. Ex merchant navy, everybody's First Mate, unless, that is, you get on the wrong side of him. He elicits sympathy from Margaret. Who could fail to be moved to compassion by his illness?

Jim could. He is honest enough to admit that he resents Davie seeking to take his father's place, but Jim thinks Davie is an arse hole nevertheless.

Davie wants to move in with Margaret. Her faith may have taken a pasting in recent years, but Margaret won't even consider living with him without God's approval. She takes his proposal very seriously, lining the children up one Sunday afternoon in the kitchen to discuss the matter.

"I am thinking about marrying him," she begins cautiously, scrutinising their faces intently for any clues. "But I want you to be completely honest with me about how you feel. I won't go through with it if any of you aren't happy about it."

What do they think? Jim thinks his mum has been to hell and back in recent years. Beth thinks noone should ever have to suffer like she has. Hugh remembers the white shock of her expression, taut with grief, after the funeral; the hand that pulled away from his. Kay? She's longing for a daddy to replace the one she lost.

46

Jim's heart is telling him to protect his mother at all costs but his head is reasoning that no one should stand in the way of Margaret's happiness, least of all him. He drops his head as he responds, unable to meet her gaze. "I think if he makes you happy, Mum, then that's all right by us."

Jim has his eye on Davie now. Davie drinks too much. He swallows too many drugs. Davie cannot be trusted even with his own prescriptions, having overdosed in the past, so Margaret has to collect them for him. Taking off her nursing uniform each night, she steps seamlessly into her next role, caring for Davie. It's a remarkably familiar one, after the years spent caring for her darling Hugh but easier too because no one expects you to be happy when you're married to a violent drunk. Being knocked sideways across the kitchen floor instantly takes your mind off your grief. Margaret hasn't been happy since Hugh died. Life has been lonely and hard and Davie is a badly needed distraction. He needs her and Margaret desperately longs to be needed. Love she has all but given up on, but need? That qualifies you for keeping going, for putting one foot in front of the other.

Jim examines Davie's Dicanol. Nothing ventured, nothing gained, he reasons, popping a pill. They make him sublimely calm and peaceful, enabling him to sleep, free of his tormented feelings.

"He's stealing ma fuckin' scripts!" Complains Davie, self-righteously.

Margaret lines them both up, side by side.

"Empty your pockets!" She demands.

Jim's, of course, are empty. He is smarter than Davie. He could run rings around Davie, he thinks smugly. Life is a pissed blur of missed opportunity for Davie. He hates Jim.

Nobody ever believes Davie, even when he is telling the truth. Worst of all, no one ever doubts Jim and therein lies the tragedy of both.

Davie is devious. He heads out to the doctor and talks him into giving him eight Palfium tablets.

"They'll last you until tomorrow evening," advises the doctor, sternly.

Two hours later, they are gone. Davie meets some mates, goes for a curry and washes all eight down with lager. Margaret is on the night shift at the hospital when they call her at 3 a.m. to tell her that her husband is lying unconscious on a bed in A&E with a stomach pump attached to him.

Davie, it seems, has no idea how to be a role model to his stepchildren.

Every ounce of hatred Jim harbours towards Davie is returned by him measure for measure. He constantly belittles Jim, widening the chasm between them, but who should Margaret trust? Jim outwits Davie on every level yet ironically not all of Davie's objections are unfounded.

"Davie says you burn that incense to hide the smell of drugs?" Margaret, hand on hip, challenges Jim from the doorway of his bedroom.

Jim bursts out laughing, briefly allaying Margaret's suspicions while inwardly cursing Davie. Until now, it has only been the weed.

Jim is watching the moon landings, sitting on the settee in the lounge. Neil Armstrong takes a giant leap for humankind just as the door bursts open and Davie staggers in from the pub. He lands promptly on the living room carpet, pissed and lost in space. Neil Armstrong combats zero gravity as Jim and Davie embark on zero tolerance, but at least they have a shared interest now. Jim is taking DF118s too.

Davie intended to return to life as a merchant seaman, but cancer prevented his getting the necessary paperwork to allow him back to sea. Now he gets the odd job on the dredgers, working the Clyde. Invariably, though, he gets sacked or walks out. Davie is an expert in sabotage; captain of his own sinking ship.

His frustration grows to epic proportions and every night the sleeping pills and pain killers are washed down with a tide of beer. Davie is setting sail for his final destination, slumped in front of the television, semicomatose, charting his course between his snores.

*

Beth, Jim's sister, is expecting her first child. She talks to him now and then, smoothing her swollen belly with the palm of her hand.

"They reckon babies can hear everything, even in the womb," she announces brightly to Jim.

She hopes fervently they are wrong about that. You wouldn't want to be getting an earful of Davie before you'd even set foot on the planet.

"Were those beef burgers before you set fire to them, Mum?" Beth grins, teasing Margaret good-naturedly over dinner.

"You shut the fuck up, do you hear me?" Davie shoves Beth viciously back down onto her chair, taking curious exception to her throwaway remark.

Everyone tenses as Beth's waters immediately break and panic ensues. An ambulance is summoned and there is a mad rush to the maternity unit. Baby Steven is born yelling his head off and who can blame him? He'll need a good set of lungs if he plans to join this household.

CHAPTER 7

Summer 1970, Jim gets busted. Two coppers stop him in the middle of Sauchiehall Street and steer him up a side road. Hands behind his back, face against the wall, they conduct an impromptu search because they never know what they might come up with. Today, they find half an ounce and moments later, Jim is sitting in a cell at the sheriff court, shaking with apprehension.

He recalls Bill Grady, up on a charge of drunk and disorderly last year.

"Fined £30," pronounces the Sheriff.

"Can I pay in instalments?" Bill queries.

"Mr. Grady, I'm here to dispense justice, not run a High Street catalogue!" The Sheriff snaps.

It seemed funny at the time.

Costly business, this drug taking. Jim is fined £25 and, to his great relief, duly released. He returns to work, aware that he has been lucky. A couple of his colleagues are encouraging him to take a closer interest in the Post Office accounting system. Nuances, such as how to declare a loss on paper while yielding a profit behind the scenes. Like all the best tricks of the trade, it's an insider secret so Jim's keeping his head down, playing his cards close to his chest. He's wishing fervently that the voice of his inner conscience would quit bending his ear.

That's done the trick. The roar of Dan's brand new motorbike revving up outside work has brightened Jim's outlook.

"What d'you reckon, mate?" Dan demands, striding over, grinning, helmet in hand.

"It's brilliant. How much did it set you back?"

Dan knowingly taps his finger against the side of his nose.

"That's between me and the profit and loss account!" He laughs uproariously. "Tough times call for tough measures, as a man at the Broo once told me!"

He doesn't care, Dan. He is blatant about fiddling the figures. If the bosses weren't half asleep, they'd wake up and smell the coffee in an instant.

Jim glances at his watch. He's on borrowed time and he knows it. He's manning the front counter today but the customers keep interrupting his LSD trip and demanding service. Exasperated, he appeals for understanding. He is being held against his will by a government employer, unsympathetic to his burgeoning drug habit. When his paranoia is at its height, he is reduced to scribbling hand written notes to whomever he happens to be serving and passing them under the glass. He can't bear to talk to anyone about it. The screen divides Jim from the outside world as effectively as his drug of choice has severed him from reality.

The Post Office is clocking on fast. Head Office summons Jim and summarily sacks him. Thanking him for his efforts, they politely invite him to pack up his desk and leave.

As one door closes, however, another duly opens. Jim's enforced vacation from working life offers a splendid opportunity to invest in a Post Office scheme of his own.

Making withdrawals proves surprisingly lucrative, especially with a former colleague on the inside. You just have to keep your nerve and hope that no-one spots your more unorthodox transactions. Jim is making a good return on his initial investment. He wonders privately why more savers don't adopt this scheme, but perhaps they are simply risk adverse.

His contact on the inside is not so sure it is a good idea. Jim is just getting into his stride when his associate panics and burns the books. Jim is disappointed, naturally, but remains philosophical.

His older brother, Hugh, has invited him to England to stay for a month. No doubt he is attempting to help him out, in the guise of a little holiday.

He won't be any trouble, Jim assures him. "You'll hardly know I'm there."

Sure enough, Jim arrives at Worthing station and is out and about almost immediately, searching out new suppliers. Most people on a wee holiday need to get their bearings at first. Jim is self-catering, after a fashion, but his needs are rather more specific than a sliced white loaf or a pint of milk.

Cough medicine keeps that persistent cough of his at bay. It's more of an internal rattle, really. The medicine wards off the shakes, while he attempts to go cold turkey. After all, he has promised them all that he will try – his mother, Beth, Kay and Hugh. They're all concerned about him. He's convinced he can give up; he just lacks the motivation.

Jim likes being near the seaside, evoking as it does such pleasant memories. Hugh and his wife are quick to make him feel at home while reminiscing over Glasgow days. But he's not been here often enough to establish a more lasting and loving connection. The Jim that they remember from when they moved out was fourteen years old. He slept on the settee when they had his old bedroom, but he would insist on going back in to do his homework every evening. They find it hard to correlate that bright fourteen year old boy with the troubled nineteen year old now staring back at them. Darkness has crept into his eyes and there are heavy circles around them. The boy is still in there somewhere, peering out, but he is increasingly walled in by a tough exterior.

Temporary relocation of Jim's habit presents him with no major problems. Dealers, it appears, get everywhere these days. A bit like the weeds that insisted on shooting up through the gaps in the concrete back in Anderston – no matter how many times you cut them back, they just keep on growing.

On the train home, Jim wonders if Hugh will miss him or if he is privately relieved that he is gone. Shrugging cynically, he folds his arms protectively around himself. He has a paper and a cup of coffee and the remnants of his cough mixture.

Clean at last, or so he convinces himself. He showed them all, didn't he? Perhaps they won't be so quick to judge him next time?

But he might as well pop into Gino's on the way back because he feels a bit lonely and fancies listening to a bit of music before heading home. He wanders up the Byres Road and sticks his head in the door. Frank is waiting for him. It's weird, that. It's almost as if he has been expecting Jim to turn up.

"Got something you might like here, Jim," Frank announces over a mug of tea and a fag.

Jim looks expectantly at the contents of Frank's pocket. The Rolling Stones are on the jukebox in the background.

"Sister Morphine," Frank smiles and casually passes a packet across the table as if Jim has merely forgotten to add sweetener to his tea.

CHAPTER 8

Jim is busy right now; he's off to see a man about a drug. The last time he saw him, Tam Munro was busily chasing 'square bubbles' off a rooftop in Govan, but thankfully today, he is more lucid.

Highly intelligent, Tam is a psychiatric nurse who has studied under R. D. Laing. Tam is always questioning, forever exploring a new approach to life. His fascination with William Burroughs and his novel, Junkie, leads Tam to experiment. Taking advantage of his professional position, he steals an ampoule of heroin and injects a sixteenth of a grain into the muscle in his thigh. It achieves nothing, so he tries an eighth and it spirals from there. There are no rigorous checks in place yet concerning the issue of drugs and the procedures that are in place are easy enough for Tam to circumnavigate.

Tam returned to Glasgow from London because he had heard there was a new scene burgeoning. The drug scene in 1960s Glasgow has become an insular, tight-knit community. Anyone taking junk almost certainly knows everyone else who is doing the same, but no one is yet bringing large amounts of opiates into Glasgow.

Tam wants a good supply. He is no longer content with small hits so he decides to rob a pharmacy. Tam starts with the hospital pharmacy where, because no one is expecting a robbery, there is little security in place. He is not particularly fussy on his first foray. Anything that is classified as a dangerous drug will do. These are kept in locked cabinets but nevertheless he manages to break them open with a spatula lying nearby.

Naturally, Tam has friends he wants to share his good fortune with. No money changes hands because that's not what friendship is about; it is more about Mother H spreading her evil by using Tam to create more dependants. Predatory spider that she is, she grows her web surreptitiously, with the aid of her willing accomplice.

It is not Tam's intention to launch a commercial enterprise but that seems to be what happens when word gets out. People appear, wanting to sample his wares. People that Tam does not like. People whom he tells to leave, in no uncertain terms. Taking offence at this, some of them drop his name to the police and he gets five years. He only serves two but when he gets out, the drug scene has fizzled out. Nobody knows how to get Class As into Glasgow, so Tam sets off again for London.

One of the converts to Tam's cause decides to take up where he has left off. He begins breaking into chemist shops to obtain large quantities of drugs. It's a communal activity, just turning a few friends on. None of them believe the rubbish in the press about how easy it is to get hooked. Until they discover the truth.

The government are of the opinion that anyone who takes drugs is in need of psychiatric care. In Glasgow, two psychiatrists are given the task of cleaning up the city after Tam's little debacle. One of them, based in the East End, is not terribly interested in treating junkies; the other is Joseph McKenzie.

Joseph McKenzie sweeps into town like Clint Eastwood, rifle poised, looking for trouble. He stubs out his cheroot in the centre of the Govan Road before setting up his clinic at the Southern General.

Jim would like very much to take him up on his offer of a hospital bed, but Joseph wants Jim to come clean first and although Jim wants to come clean too, he's not quite ready yet. He has a chemist shop to break into first. He guesses, quite correctly, that Joseph doesn't want to hear about it.

The trouble with a really bad drug habit is the escalating cost. There is an abscess on Jim's arm now and a burning hole in his pocket. Had he known all this earlier, he would of course have made suitable provisions. Except nobody predicted he'd be an addict when he grew up.

In the dark, he climbs through the skylight of his local pharmacy while the others stand guard. They emerge seconds later with a sizeable haul. Opiates, barbiturates and a bottle of Lucozade; got to keep your strength up on the night shift. Swinging the torch around, they race back home. It's surprisingly quiet out on the streets tonight, not even a hint of sirens.

The Drug Squad have to be Monty Python fans to a man. They descend like the Spanish Inquisition on the house of Jim's associate. They've developed an uncanny knack for establishing who will cave in under pressure first and their instincts are rarely wrong. Soon enough, they arrive at West Princes Street.

Jim's mother, Margaret, is startled at their request to search the premises.

"We have a warrant," the officer advises her.

"But I've just hoovered," she replies in exasperation, staring at his boots.

Margaret is far from happy. Why do they need to upturn all the cushions on the settee again? She only plumped them up this morning. And surely there is no need to dismantle the cistern in the bathroom?

It's a mystery to Jim how those packets of morphine and cocaine came to be in his mother's flat, not least because he knows for certain he didn't put them there. He loves her too much to ever expose her to the risks of his habit.

Integrity, it seems, is in short supply all round. The Drug Squad, it appears, have come prepared, carrying props of their own. Charged with possession, Jim feels disadvantaged, not least because that very morning, Joseph called him to offer him a bed at the Southern General.

Joseph intervenes and pleads with the police on Jim's behalf. They are keen to incarcerate him, but Joseph knows that it's the hospital bed that holds the solution to Jim's problems, not a prison cell. The Drug Squad are not happy at being outmanoeuvred. You can tell by the way they eye Jim threateningly on their way out.

"You'll keep, Sonny," they whisper to him.

Joseph is one of the good guys. He is on the same side as Bud Neill's legendary cartoon hero, Lobey Dosser. His aim is to clean up the mean streets of Glasgow. Determining to drive the evil 'Rank Bajin' far from the city, Joseph is discovering that there are more of them than he first suspected and that they have many disguises at their disposal as they sit in the wings, biding their time.

CHAPTER 9

"Hi, Jim, how you doing?"

Annie is waiting in the corridor for him after the clinic.

Jim is quite attracted to Annie, truth be told, not that he lets her know that. They are both seeing someone else at the moment, namely Joseph McKenzie. Annie has drug issues of her own. She stays with mutual friends, Claire and Ian, and Jim often drops by. It's been a place to use drugs, until now. Could it also prove to be a launch pad for romance?

Jim? He could take it or leave it really. Well, that's what he lets her think. He could never admit he is too intimidated to even chance his arm.

Luckily for him, she decides to take matters into her own hands one evening, when they are both stoned. He emerges from her bed the next morning a changed man, confident that he has her where he wants her, but the trouble is, a bit like the dope, he's hooked now. One taste and he can't retreat. He wants her, more and more.

And Annie? What does Annie want? What does she see, beyond the chance to score drugs? Does she even notice Jim lying there beside her in the warmth?

His friends try to warn him off her because they can see that she's no good but Jim's not interested in health warnings, not when Annie is seemingly so impressed that he is out scoring for her and not when she makes it abundantly clear she wants to sleep with him.

Except that even now, Jim is lying to himself. He isn't scoring; he never was. He is taking from his own stash – the remnants of the chemist break in – the packets that the Drug Squad failed to uncover. Annie is mad as hell once she discovers this. Jim is diminished in her eyes because he is no bad boy dealer after all. She leaves for Edinburgh and Jim, feeling lost, takes to his bed, but fortunately for all concerned, he takes Joseph's advice this time and chooses a hospital bed. Joseph's intention is to keep him there for as long as it takes to reduce his drug intake.

But Jim is restless, and college beckons. That's the answer. He will study hard and go to university. Joseph's not best pleased. It means his planned hospital admission is cut short but Jim is determined. So he is discharged, with a prescription.

"You're going to have to take great care," Joseph cautions. He gets the sense he is repeating himself. Jim listens, but his mind is elsewhere, focused on a repeat prescription.

It's a lot to fit in, studying for Highers while keeping an eye on his supply of uppers and downers. Punctuating college with the odd court appearance, Jim duly does his best. The lecturers might not appreciate the efforts he has to go to to conceal his double life, but his mate Liam understands. Liam is American and is also into junk. Most of the time he is utterly disinterested in anything, which makes him undemanding company.

Jim, on the other hand, is totally absorbed in one particular subject. She is a willowy beauty by the name of Claire and she is going out with Ian. A pity that, because Jim is convinced she should be seeing him instead.

It is January 1972 when Jim appears in court on the morphine and cocaine charges. Farcical, really, the legislative process. They are charging him for possession of drugs that the Drug Squad planted on him in order for the Drug Squad to obtain justice for something he actually did do that they were unable to prove. Honestly, it's enough to make you bitter, if you let it. Snow White they are not. The cocaine cloud of powdery doubt hangs over Jim though; but for that, he would be quite tempted to point the finger at them himself.

"If you don't plead guilty, they'll throw the book at you," his solicitor advises.

So what choice does he have? He is remanded in Barlinnie Prison for three weeks, pending background reports. Until now, Jim has never had any problem with bad reports. He has been a straight A student. This is the first time he has run the risk of receiving a discouraging report in his entire life. Worse still, he is withdrawing. Incarceration in an observation cell, in the hospital wing at Barlinnie, requires him being alone for twenty four hours a day for a week. Three days in, going cold turkey, he is seriously questioning his sanity. As the drugs wear off, his whole body is seized with tremors and every muscle aches interminably. Jim, who has not shed a tear since his father died, cries himself to sleep at night. What are the voices he hears, alone in the dark? He daren't tell anyone how bad it is. It is a terrible descent, like slipping into the very pit of hell itself.

He emerges onto a ward with ten or twelve others for the remaining two weeks. He is scared and still withdrawing, and totally freaked out when he hears raised voices chanting in unison, hands banging the walls.

"The Billy Boys will be here soon. Fuck the Pope and Tommy Doone!"

The singing grows in pitch as the old lag himself arrives on the scene.

"You all right there, son?" The friendly face of Tommy Doone enquires genially. Jim is relieved. Tommy takes it upon himself to take Jim under his wing and warns off the hatchet faced Doyle who has been gunning for him since he arrived on the ward. Doyle scowls, but defers to Doone's assessment of the situation. Tommy Doone, God love him; you wouldn't cross him. He's short but powerfully built. He's seen some sights, has Tommy Doone.

Once on remand, the Sheriff decides to replace Jim's college lectures for the afternoon with one of his own courthouse lectures. It wasn't time tabled, but it's in Jim's best interests to listen politely.

"You deserve to go to jail," he booms, self-righteously. "But, fortunately for you, I have taken on board Mr. McKenzie's advice and decided to defer sentence."

Jim's legs nearly give way beneath him, so great is his relief. The enforced rehabilitation programme has taken its toll on his body. He is weak and his joints ache maddeningly.

Jim's friend Terry has the answer. He has saved Jim a hit for when he gets out, just like he promised he would.

Joseph McKenzie is furious. He thumps the desk that stands between him and Jim. "What the hell did you think you were playing at? You're a bloody idiot, so you are!"

Resentfully he signs Jim's script and dismisses him from his sight. Jim feels a twinge of regret at having let him down. Joseph is right, he is an idiot, but Joseph knows too that without the script it would be downhill all the way for Jim.

Jim is dreaming of Claire now. Pinch him and make sure he's awake, because he thinks she just smiled at him, one of her special smiles that she reserves for when Ian's not looking. There it is again. God, she's beautiful tonight.

The conversation is barbed all the way with barbiturates and Claire. He can't get enough of them both. He deliberates swiftly and decides to seize his chance, leaning forward when he has her on his own at last, taking her face in his hands and kissing her gently on the lips. She responds in a way that shows she is not startled by his interest.

He can hardly believe it. He is walking on air. As Ian descends into the lounge again, they fling themselves apart and Jim pretends to read the sleeve notes of an album. Claire is flushed, which only adds to her appeal. He winks at her, she beams back and Ian, God love him, never notices.

As they leave, he sneaks a glance at her and they both know it then. They are an item. He goes to bed alone, but lies awake, gazing into the darkness. A tender peace surrounds him in which he can see only her auburn hair and green eyes that stare gently into his.

CHAPTER 10

"Ian ought to keep the noise down," Jim warns Claire. "He'll have the whole street awake in a minute!"

You can't go around ranting and raving outside other people's houses late at night. It's hardly dignified. Jim opens the sash window and glowers down at Ian. "She's not coming out, mate. Go home!"

"You – ya fucking bastard! This is all your fault!" Ian is shaking his fist at Jim from down below.

Jim closes the window decisively and lights up a fag. Claire is pleading at him with her eyes. He looks away.

"Claaiire..." Ian sets up whining, with all the appeal of a stray dog in a police pound. Swinging an empty Irn Bru bottle in his hand, he seems to be weighing up whether to hurl it at the glass.

"Don't wind him up, eh, Jim?" Claire puts her shoes on.

"You're not going down to him?" Jim is aghast.

Claire throws her coat on. "What else can I do? Your mum's not going to thank me when she has to get up for work in the morning is she?"

Jim is mortally wounded, but she has a point.

He watches dismally from the window as Claire walks out. She calms Ian down and gets up to speed on what is happening in Ian-World. Maddeningly frustrated at not being able to hear what they are saying to each other, he waits impatiently for her to return. He can scarcely believe his eyes when he sees her glance back up at the window, eyebrows raised towards him, signalling that she has to walk Ian back home. He's in a dreadful state.

Where does Claire get off? Jim knows she finds it hard to take sides but can't she see it tears him in two when she does this? On the other hand, he has brought it on himself, seducing somebody else's girlfriend, only now he's left to deal with the avalanche of feelings unleashed in him. He doesn't do tears. He is not like Ian, crying all the way down West Princes Street. He decides to give Claire an ultimatum the next time he sees her.

"You don't go back to him anymore!" He rants at her, raising his hand in frustration. He feels even more dreadful after that. It does nothing to alleviate the volcano of anger he is sitting on. He is at boiling point and what scares him is not knowing what's underneath all the anger.

Claire, she just wants a quiet life. She shifts from Ian's spare room to Jim's mum's flat and back again. A United Nations envoy brokering a peace deal scarcely had a tougher task. She doesn't need this, not while she has a drug habit to attend to.

Jim has been charged with possession in the past but all his attempts to possess Claire are doomed to failure. He wants her all to himself, but Ian insists on sharing her affections. Ian can scream and shout the odds all he wants, but this is only going to end one way.

It's not easy, living in the middle of a war zone. It's doing Claire's head in. Staring into Jim's questioning eyes, then being haunted by Ian's distraught face.

One morning she disappears. Jim and Ian are forced to confer for the first time in ages. They have a mutual need to know she is safe. Claire lies in a hospital bed at the Southern General, trying to get her head straight. She has had herself admitted overnight, desperate to clean up her act, wanting help to discharge everything from her system – the drugs, the upsets, the betrayals.

Sat by her bed, holding her hand, Jim tells her he's sorry and means it. He never intended it would lead to this. She sighs and gives him that gentle smile of hers. Awash on a sea of despondency, she hardly knows what to do for the best but she loves him too, in her own way. She is the pale, ethereal ghost who haunts the dark corridors of his imagination. He leaves without her, but she is forever etched on his heart.

It's a trust exercise. Jim tries to figure out what the examiner is looking for but he has no special insights. He can only hope that by showing his inner workings, he will gain extra points for his efforts. Jim hates being defeated by tests of any kind and it's not in his nature to give up. You'd like to think that Jim would put Claire ahead of the drugs and indeed he does his best. Alphabetically at least, she is way in front of the Opiates. Heroin has nothing on her. Only barbiturates are a front runner and they were what gave him the nerve to ask her out in the first place.

He lies in bed, staring at the ceiling for hours, thinking about her, recalling her heart beat pounding against his chest when he held her in his arms. What if she won't come back to him? How will he manage without her now? He couldn't face a withdrawal alone.

Take a wild stab in the dark. Is there a link here between Jim's need of drugs and his need of Claire? Is one more torturous than the other? Right now he'd crawl over broken glass to get to either. He craves both but is willing to relinquish neither. Love, it seems, has rarely been less of a blessing. It is only adding to his pain.

Claire bows to the greater good. She returns to live in Ian's spare room on the condition that he allows her to pursue her relationship with Jim unchallenged. As compromises go, it stinks. It solves nothing. She is invariably late for her dates with Jim. Suspicion burns in him, however apologetic she is. It's enough to drive a man to drink, this relationship – if it wasn't for the fact he is already on heroin.

CHAPTER 11

Margaret, having worked extra shifts at the hospital, has fairly worn herself out and is admitted for an overnight stay herself, courtesy of the General Hospital. Life with Davie has exhausted her. Pernicious anaemia is the consultant's diagnosis. He might just have saved Margaret's life by admitting her promptly; his timing, did he know it, is impeccable.

It is comparatively peaceful on the ward. Margaret exhales deeply, grateful for the rest and stares at a painting of children playing near a highland stream on the wall opposite. Where did it all go wrong? She longs to ask the doctor as he pauses with his stethoscope to discuss her blood counts, but even he doesn't look as if he has all the answers.

"Try not to worry," he smiles, patting her hand. "We'll have you out of here in no time."

That's precisely what Margaret is concerned about.

Back at home, Davie has been kicking up for hours. He staggers in from the pub, long after last orders, stinking of drink and cigarette smoke, his trousers stained with urine. He wildly wags a finger in Claire's face and threatens to stove Jim's head in. Fists waving, he punches the living room wall as he attempts to exorcize his demons. What's eating Davie? What hurts him so much that he cannot help but spew forth bile and hatred at the world? Cancer is eating away at him from the inside out. A physical manifestation of all that is inwardly amiss. He is desperate to announce his plight to the world, but the world won't listen. The world is constantly turning its back on Davie and he is furious about it. He intends to let the fucking world have it, tonight, with both barrels.

Davie gathers his balance and gestures drunkenly in Jim's direction. "I wanna word with you, ya gobshite!"

"Well, I'm not interested in having a word with you!" Jim counters, with feeling. Claire tenses, curled up beside him on the settee, afraid of where this is leading.

Davie, undeterred, grabs a chair. Turning it the wrong way around, he perches on it in a bizarre parody of Christine Keeler's famous pose. Nobody is laughing.

"And I'm tellin' you, I'm gonna talk to you!" Davie seizes control again, his tone sinister now. Does he think he is still addressing a barroom of angry drinkers? Does he even realise he is back at home? He is looking for trouble, but Jim isn't having any of it. He can't hit a sick man, though; his conscience won't allow it. Damn his conscience to hell. What good did it ever do him, he thinks, bitterly. Davie needs some sense knocking into him. Jim steers him determinedly out of the room. Pushing past him, he retrieves Claire's coat from the stand in the hall. Davie slithers down the wall, half crying, half full of rage.

"You'd better go," Jim tells Claire, helping her on with her coat. She is secretly relieved as he walks her back to Ian's place but he dreads returning home, expecting the worst. The flat is strangely silent. Jim swallows two strong sleeping pills and goes out like a light as soon as his head hits the pillow, grateful for the respite.

Davie has finally crashed out asleep on the bed, but wakes briefly and staggers into the bathroom, swiping wildly at an imaginary foe on his way back down the hall. He slides back into bed, barely registering the gap next to him where Margaret should be. He lights a cigarette. Then he sinks into a deep sleep. His hand drags across the bed and falls over the side, the fag end still glowing red.

"Jim! Jim! Open your fucking door!"

Jim appears, bleary eyed, to find Beth frantically barging in on Davie.

"The flat's on fucking fire! Get out!"

Jim stares back at her for a split second, then throws on his dressing gown. She is halfway down the hall with Steven under her arm. Kay is racing after her. Jim bangs furiously on Davie's door, but there is no response. He hates him, true enough, but he would never leave him to die.

"Get up, Davie! Get the fuck out! The flat's on fire!"

Blue-black flames burst forth from the room as Jim attempts to enter. Thick smoke chokes his lungs, making it impossible to breathe. He throws his sleeve across his mouth, his chest bursting with the effort to keep going.

"Jim! NO! Leave it!" Beth turns back, yelling at him.

Jim is battling on. Grabbing a towel, he holds it to his face and attempts again to get into Davie's room. A furnace blast of heat nearly knocks him off his feet. Davie is already lost to the hellish flames. It is blisteringly hot. Jim charges outside. Just in time.

The fire brigade arrive, sirens blazing. The family, safe inside the neighbour's flat, sit drinking hot sweet tea; their shaking hands rattle the bone china. The noise and commotion seem eerie and unreal. Kay shivers in an armchair. Beth is struggling to compose herself. They put their arms around each other, relieved to be alive.

Nervously the chief fireman enters. He removes his helmet. An act of respect. He perches on the arm of the settee.

"Is your mother here?"

"She's in hospital," Jim replies.

Steven, large eyed and solemn, gazes up at the fireman. Beth clutches the boy tightly to her.

"I'm afraid I have some very bad news. I'm terribly sorry. We did all we could to try to save your stepfather, but I'm afraid it was too late."

He is not prepared for their reaction.

"Ach, sure that's a shame. Really, it might have been better for him to go under a bus."

Beth is semi-hysterical. Jim almost wets himself laughing. The poor fireman stands between them, utterly bewildered. It's shock, of course, he understands that. How could they ever hope to explain to him what the last few years of hell have been like?

They return to the flat. It stinks of smoke, their mother's bedroom gutted, blackened and barely recognisable. No one can hope to get any sleep. They sink down side by side in the living room. In silence. In the early hours of the morning, Jim decides to go for a walk. He is just about to step into the street, when a flashlight goes off suddenly in his face.

A journalist rushes over, notepad in hand. "We heard someone died here last night. Is that right, lad?".

Jim is taken aback. "Yes, my stepfather."

"Can you give us all the details?" The journalist presses him.

Jim feels terrible. He desperately wants to be left alone and he badly needs his prescription. He hates the press intruding like this. Have they no idea what his family have just been through?

Later that morning, Claire makes her way to the launderette. While waiting for the spin cycle to finish, she pops across the road to pick up a paper. As she walks back across one of the busiest roads in Glasgow, she is greeted by the headline: 'Man Dies In City Fire.' There is a photograph of Jim directly beneath it. Claire stops dead in the middle of the road. Jim? Her Jim? Dead? Drivers blast their horns as they swerve to avoid her. She makes it to the pavement in time to discover it is Davie, not Jim, who has died.

With Margaret still in hospital, it is left to Jim and Beth to go and identify Davie's body. When they arrive at the coroner's office, Jim is drugged up, full of false bravado. Beth is nervous. Daft really. Since they both disliked him intensely they should be relieved, not sad, shouldn't they? But now he is gone and reality is a bugger. No matter what you thought of someone when they were alive, when you witness them lying stone cold on a slab, skin blackened and charred, features barely recognisable, your heart goes out to them. Jim is nearly sick. He can't get out of there fast enough. He retreats, pale and shaking to the corridor.

His own father had looked peaceful at the end. The same cannot be said of Davie.

CHAPTER 12

What kind of homecoming is this? Margaret has barely recovered her strength from the hospital ward when she is discharged. Contemplating the empty armchair where Davie once sat, she can barely comprehend the horror of all that has happened. Worse still, her own parents are not here to comfort her this time around. There is, it seems, for Margaret, no reprieve. No let up anywhere along the line. She can't take it anymore.

Jim studies her face intently. It is hard to tell if there is a living soul inside his mother anymore. She carries winter in her bones, shivering, even with the heating on, because there is no intrinsic warmth left in her life. She tries to reason her way out of it. At least Davie is no longer suffering; the cancer did not get its way a second time. Her children are alive, thank God, but Margaret is a shell of her former self, emptied of purpose, her life ruined. She wipes her spectacles, replaces them, stares into space.

In the end, she moves out, using the insurance proceeds to buy a new property further down the road.

Jim keeps her flat on. Margaret says it's bad luck, the flat, but Jim doesn't believe in luck. He believes in random occurrences, like Claire moving in with him.

Love has shone its light into Jim's life at last. He is in a rare state of bliss, waking each morning with Claire's autumnal head on the pillow beside his, her emerald eyes twinkling mischievously at him as she draws him into a kiss. They don't have two pennies to rub together, but star gazing and dreaming are free. Even the government doesn't have the heart to charge for them.

Of course it doesn't last. She gets restless. Ian and his mates are off to Morocco.

"Come with me!" She demands, hurling a pillow playfully over Jim's head.

He wrestles free of her. "What with?" He demands.

He is heartbroken that she is going. It's not just the money. He can't go through with being without drugs again, not after Barlinnie. It was hell.

There's nothing going on between her and Ian, she assures Jim. But can he truly trust her? She kisses him as she leaves, holding him as if she will be gone forever. He might as well face facts. He will never see her again.

He closes the door and leans against the wall, fighting back the urge to cry. The silence she left behind is deafening.

The Marrakesh Express has rolled into town and taken his woman aboard. All he can do is watch it disappear into the distance amid a haze of dope smoke and wonder if he will ever see her again.

The flat is intolerable without her. It's too large for one thing and too full of memories for another. His dad's ailing face in one room, Davie's charred body in another, too many ruined Christmasses and false 'new starts'.

Liam from college and his brother Frank, are looking for somewhere to stay and Jim jumps at the opportunity. He needs the company and they need a base. They are doing a lot of dealing in junk. They opt to pay the rent in kind, which wouldn't be so bad if it wasn't for the fact that Jim is often called upon to find veins. It hardly helps his own habit, drawing him into temptation, catching him in a weak moment. He's had many of those since Claire left.

At least some people bother to keep in touch regularly. Say what you like about the Drug Squad, they are loyal at least, they haven't left Jim alone since Liam and Frank appeared on the scene. They know the score better than the two brothers themselves. Not that they have been able to prove anything yet, but that doesn't stop them attempting their raids in the small hours. They skip the country in the end, Liam and Frank. They can take a hint; they know when they're not welcome.

Eventually the doorbell goes again. Perhaps the Drug Squad is adopting social niceties at last? But no! He would recognise that auburn head of hair anywhere!

"Claire?"

"Jim? Oh God!" The shock of seeing him again. She throws her arms around him, but the tears on her face are not prompted by joy.

"Claire?" He is shaking with relief. He thought she'd gone for good. He'd resigned himself to never seeing her again. She appears like a beautiful dream to his troubled eyes. He wonders privately if she is real or if he will wake up to find this moment cruelly snatched from him.

"Jim, you look terrible."

He hangs his head, ashamed. He is mortified that she is seeing him like this. His clothes are shabby and unwashed, his hair greasy, hanging down the side of his face. But he loves her. If only she could see inside his heart, she wouldn't doubt that for a moment. She makes him a cup of tea. It should be him doing it for her, but she has bustled into the kitchen, working her way through seven days worth of dishes lying in the sink. She is bagging up the rubbish and sticking it outside for the council to collect. She opens a window.

"Let some air in, eh?" She throws him a broken smile.

She is sorry she ever left him on his own. All the light of Marrakesh is diminished, snuffed out like a candle, now she is back on Scottish soil. Is it the dank, dishwater days? Did they wipe out all his good intentions?

He has plans for them both. He is eager to confide them, but he senses now is not the time. She loves him deeply, but she can't hang around forever, not at her age. Not if she wants to start a family. He will have to make a decision sooner or later, or she will make it for him. She is tight-lipped on this right now. He needs her desperately, she can see that.

"I'm so sorry, Jim. I'm going to make it up to you, I promise." She is as good as her word.

While Jim is in pieces, feeling terrible that he has let Claire down yet again, Claire is vibrant and strong. She has stopped using. She is determined Jim will too. She moves back in with him, concentrating all her efforts on getting him back to normal – normal being only using the prescription that Joseph McKenzie gives him, without the optional extras.

But Claire doesn't have the willpower to steer clear herself, not now she's back in amongst it all, far from the sunny skies of Marrakesh. The slate grey clouds and interminable rain of Glasgow convince her it is not worth the effort. She gives in at last and returns to Joseph McKenzie to get another prescription.

Ian is less of a threat now; the battle lines once drawn between them have been erased by time and experience.

Life becomes a game of musical chairs, as Ian moves in with them both. Claire then makes up her mind to get clean and exits stage left to Oban. Ian moves out. Claire comes back to Jim at weekends, bringing him records from the shop where she works. Each time she goes, he retreats into his books and listens to records for hours on end. Scared by the enormity of the loss he feels, he is prescribed Valium which messes up his memory.

During the winter, Claire moves back in with Jim, Oban being too isolated in a frozen season, and gets a job as a model at the local art school. Jim loves her. He needs her. Her distant, dreamy face, and faraway eyes haunt him. He makes a serious effort to smarten up his act. New clothes, brightens himself up, fresh and clean this time. He tidies up the flat, looks for a job, starts a college course, part time. But he is operating through a haze of Valium and Methadone, papering over the cracks of his fears that he has suppressed for so long that they have become an abyss. One that he is terrified of falling into.

Jim is only comfortable in the company of his friends. His friends are only comfortable in the company of junk. Claire wants more than this for herself and Jim. While she wants to settle down, he has a longing to be free. Or rather, did he but realise it, he has a longing to run away from the terrifying emotions bottled up inside him.

In the end, Claire has no choice but to cut and run. She goes to work in a hotel outside Glasgow and returns to see him once a fortnight. He phones her a lot in between, when he is not too busy. Busy that is, crushing tablets into powder and injecting them into his arms.

CHAPTER 13

How long has he been lying here, gazing up at the ceiling? The milk, abandoned in the bottle on the kitchen work surface has long since soured, as have Jim's good intentions. He hasn't eaten in days; he is barely even drinking. Do the neighbours not wonder how he is? Has Jim withdrawn from daily life to the extent that he no longer needs anyone? Does his mother keep her distance because she can no longer bear to watch her son destroying himself? She is, after all, a nurse; she can be under no illusions about what is happening to him.

There is always an ulterior motive behind an addict's actions. The perpetual need to seek a fix wipes out all thoughts of integrity. But locked in, with his sizeable pharmaceutical haul, Jim isn't dealing. He is not prepared to enter into negotiations with the outside world. Heroin and Jim have reached stalemate. Neither one is prepared to give any ground. So it's just Jim and his needles – the syringe and the stylus – competing for his affections now. Dr John the Night Tripper is on the turntable – New Orleans voodoo music at its finest and darkest. Do the neighbours ever think to complain about the noise or have they, too, given up?

The aching melancholy of his music, of Love's *Alone Again Or*. And Jim is alone, truly alone, hemmed in by his habit. A trail of unwashed dishes marks the spot where he ceased to care. The dust motes, suspended in the sunlight, haunt a living room festooned with a dizzying swirl of seventies wallpaper. A bad trip all round.

He tries to lure himself back to life with his record collection, but even his beloved songwriters are struggling to convince him it is worth the pain. The record sticks on the turntable. It no longer prompts him to get up and prevent its incessant repetition. The repetition no longer grates on his nerves.

Jim's veins have collapsed and now he is reduced to straining his pills through cotton and injecting directly into his muscles instead. His right arm is huge, a swollen balloon, a travesty of a limb, three times its normal size.

Dark eyes, suspicious of unwelcome callers, greet Terry Cullen at the door. He has been ringing the bell for ages.

"Hi there. I've come to see Jim. Is he in? Jim? Sorry, man, I wouldn't have recognised you! You're in a bad way, pal. How long has your arm been like that? Good job your Uncle Terry's here, eh?"

"I'm all right," Jim begins defensively.

"Aye and ma head buttons up the back, pal. You need to see a doctor, son, and sharpish. Seriously. You're coming to A & E."

Jim shakes his head. Embarrassment clouds his judgement. Pride rises up and places a sting on his heart. He wants to cry, but he never can. Everything is stuck deep inside him. It weighs him down permanently. He is exhausted from heaving the burden of his pain around with him. He has no energy anymore. Heroin has robbed him of his self-respect and left him beaten up and abandoned. Feeling deeply unloved, he is unable to see his way in life or figure it out anymore.

Terry lifts the stylus gently from the vinyl and switches the record player off. He refuses to leave, insisting that Jim must go to the General straight away. Jim steadfastly refuses. Terry casts an eye over him, regretfully.

"Promise me you'll go to the hospital, Jim, once I'm gone?" He pushes a five pound note towards him. Jim nods, and shows him out.

He is plagued with guilt, once Terry leaves. Barely able to summon the energy to make the call, he rings for a taxi. Slumped in the back of the cab, he makes it to the General Hospital. Nothing on him but the fare and the clothes he stands up in. No-one to pack him an overnight bag. If Jim doesn't care about himself, it follows logically that no one else will. He collapses in the corridor as soon as he arrives at Accident and Emergency.

Had Terry not bothered to call round that afternoon, he would have died alone among the debris in the flat.

Jim is propped up in bed, conscious at last. He listens intently to the doctor's grave analysis. "We found every known variant of bacteria in your arm. You'll be on multiple penicillin for a couple of weeks to fight the effects. We'll have to strap your arm up to prevent the infection spreading."

He pauses, checking Jim is taking all of this in.

"You've been incredibly lucky this time, son. You very nearly lost your arm."

Jim does not feel lucky. None of his problems have been solved. The demons that brought him to this place have merely retreated to regroup and discuss their next strategy for attack. He whiles away the time, staring into space.

He appreciates his mother's visits. Tirelessly, she appears at his side every day at two o'clock. Familiar with the routine setting of the hospital ward, Margaret is calm and efficient. They talk about the weather, about Mrs. Burns up the road, about the WRVS. Anything except what is truly bothering them both. Never a mention of his father, though they both crave him dearly. Jim's mum is quietly drinking on the side. Jim is figuring how he will get his next fix.

The next day he is in agony. The poison from his suspended arm has turned it septic. Surgeons perform an emergency procedure to remove vast quantities of muscle from his shoulder. It was a mistake, admit the hospital, tying his arm up like that.

"You were lucky this time son," pronounces the same doctor the next day on ward rounds. "You nearly lost that arm."

Jim contemplates life without his right arm. The loss of an entire set of dependable veins. Unthinkable to a junkie.

Perhaps, in retrospect, the doctor has a point. He has been lucky, this time.

Chapter 14

You'd think he'd call a halt now, wouldn't you? He nearly lost an arm, for crying out loud. You can't pay a much higher price than that, can you? The dealers are not just demanding money from their clients – it's limbs too; it's lives. They might as well be forcing them to stare death in the face. However hard they try to look away, they rarely succeed.

Jim can't stop. He is beyond help. He carries on injecting. Into his leg this time. Another abscess. You'd think by now that other people would have given up on Jim, but you'd be wrong. They demonstrate tremendous staying power, some of his 'friends'. They just aren't prepared to stand idly by, while Jim sinks ever downward. Well, not without making damn sure he's found them a workable vein to use first. Naturally they don't expect him to work for nothing. His field of expertise is valuable and they pay him handsomely; in kind, of course.

Jim is in the grip of suicidal feelings now. He can't see a way out. He harbours strange thoughts. No one would miss him, would they? The heroin has become a noose around his neck that will surely kill him soon anyway. He wonders if it would be better to speed up the whole process but something deep within him is inexplicably keeping him going.

Two brothers, Adam and Joe move in. He wants some company – they want a safe deposit for the proceeds of their chemist break-ins. They are generous to a fault, Adam and Joe, particularly if they've had a good day.

Jim gets out and about a bit nowadays which is surely a good thing? Except that the Dopers Pad in Napiershall Street is his home from home. He uses his influence where necessary, lording it over the new crowd there, resting back on his hard earned reputation. He and a young girl have a bit of fling there, but it's sordid stuff; he wants her body, she wants his drugs. Everything is reduced to the level of trade now, even relationships. You can't trust anyone, Jim reflects grimly; they all want something from you.

Of course he feels bad about it. Who wouldn't? Things look up briefly when Adam and Joe move out because they've upset a fair few people during their time here and Jim is relieved the heat will now be off. He can kick back and relax with Claire and his friend, Arthur. One evening, they are settling down together, by the fire, when the doorbell goes. Exasperated, Jim peers out the window.

There are twelve of them. He recognises Ray Doyle, a real head case, among their number. This doesn't look good. They haven't come here carol singing, that's for sure. A crash at the door indicates they are not prepared to wait long for an answer. They are kicking it down now. He races downstairs in time to see a metal tipped boot appear on his side of the door frame, splintering the wood in two.

"Where's Adam and Joe?" Ray rants in Jim's face, squaring up to him, his breath foul-smelling and tinged with alcohol.

Jim stares him down, steely eyed. "They're not here."

"Yes, they are. Pair of cunts. Bring them out."

"They've gone, I'm telling you."

"And I'm telling you, Pal, they'd better not have taken their wee haul with them." He shoves past Jim. "C'mon lads, get to searching the premises. Oh, and by the way, Jim, we're not bothered wi' a fucking warrant like the Drug Squad are!"

Arthur and Claire are on the landing. Arthur races down to Jim just as Ray catches sight of Claire. She looks so fragile, her auburn hair hanging loosely down to her shoulders, her eyes fraught with anxiety. Ray is not the only one who notices her. He grins slyly up at her, then motions to his henchmen.

Jim and Arthur are surrounded, hurled into the spare room and forced up against a wall. Jim makes for the door, desperate to protect Claire, just as a fist launches itself out of nowhere into his face. Six of them are on him, kicking and punching him to the floor. He can just make out Arthur's face beside him as someone connects their boot to it. Blood spatters out as they split his lip. They hold him to the ground every time he attempts to get up.

All over the house there is the sound of furniture being overturned. Jim hears a lamp being hurled out of a window and smashing on the pavement outside. Chairs are thrown aside, drawers emptied, wardrobes yanked open and their contents abandoned on the carpet.

Jim staggers to his feet and races for the door again before they can stop him. He charges into the next room, knowing already what he will see. Claire is on the floor, her expression one of raw terror. The guy standing over her has a knife to her throat.

The noise is unbelievable. It surrounds him and only afterwards does he realise that it was coming from him. An agony of rage spills out of him. They drag him backwards, seven or eight of them, pinioning his arms back, nearly yanking them out of his sockets. The door closes behind him. Of course he knows. He knows what they have done.

After they have gone, there is no going back.

CHAPTER 15

Everything inside Jim is dead. He sits on the settee night times at his sister Beth's house in Partick, blindly staring into the television set, long after close down. The piercing noise of the signal no longer reaches his ears. The picture on the screen has shrunk to a tiny square dot which in turn is swallowed by blackness, but the images in Jim's head never go away. He sees a girl with auburn hair and emerald green eyes, pleading with him to make them stop. He could not. Now it is too late.

She has left now. She will never again be by his side. Life for Jim has lost all meaning and he has no idea how to move forward.

The flat on West Princes Street became derelict and the council pulled it down in the end. There is an empty space, like a cavity where a once rotten tooth has been yanked out, and the rest of the street closes around it, concealing the extraction.

Two years pass. The snows fall steadily all winter, then the ground thaws and the spring sunshine briefly lights the pavements in a blaze of gold. The cycle begins all over again, with or without Jim's participation. Shards of ice remain riven deep in his heart. They pierce his eyes. He can no longer see what is good or worthy about himself or anyone else. The mirror that heroin created has nearly completed its demonic work. It has distorted his view of the world so thoroughly that it is now attempting to destroy his very soul.

Jim's mother still believes in God, just about. Maybe if you ask her, she is still secretly praying for Jim? Hands clasped together at night, beneath the bedclothes, face contorted with the grief of watching her son destroy himself. What can she do? What can God do, but send His angels to watch over him?

They arrive in surprising forms. This being Glasgow, and such things being frowned upon in a climate of cynicism, they might not be readily recognised in their earthly form.

Take Jim's friend, Arthur, for example. He is a tall gangly man, with a benign expression and a predilection for whisky.

"When shit turns to gold, the poor will be born without arse-holes," he proclaims confidently on the back of a postcard addressed to Jim.

The front shows the beautiful wrought-iron gates to the holy temple in Jodhpur. The self styled Lord Arthur has returned from his travels. He went east to find whatever missing fragments of his soul he had failed to locate in Glasgow. Arthur's semiconscious insights are now littered all over the hippie trail in India. Good luck to them, grins Jim. May it heap blessings upon them!

Arthur is living at the Mistry's house in the West End of Glasgow. He used to go out with their daughter and has remained a firm family friend. He emerges now and then from his basement flat, several days of beard growth on his chin. Rather like an eccentric, cave dwelling hermit; the kind that Victorian gentlefolk would pay to add a touch of interest to a garden grotto.

"Jim! Good to see you, sir!" He claps Jim cheerily on the shoulder, delightedly. He possesses all the social ease of one gentleman inviting another to his private club. "Take your time, Jimbo, there's plenty more where this one came from." He waggles an empty beer can tantalisingly under Jim's nose.

In these rare moments, Jim is perfectly at ease. He laughs uproariously at Arthur's antics. He is a wonderful friend, witty, warm and generous to a fault. But Arthur has a few bad habits, and one of them is junk. It means Jim is now sharing his script with him in an attempt to keep him from going out scoring. Jim gave Arthur his first hit; he owes it to him to keep him safe. Arthur keeps no such score of things. This is true friendship, undeserved grace.

The Mistry's house is beautiful. Surrounded by vast towering trees front and back, the living room windows run from ceiling to floor, and Mackintosh roses are etched in the corners of the glass. Vast bookshelves line the walls. Photographs of India are displayed on the mantelpiece. An air of peaceful seclusion prevails. Professor Mistry is busy at his desk and Gita, his wife, is warm and inviting, forever cooking Indian delicacies and insisting that Jim and Arthur sit down with her to eat.

Lightly spiced cauliflower, chapattis, chick pea curries and dhal. It is amazing stuff, but it is the heart food that Jim finds so nourishing. The warmth and love, unseen beneath the hot dishes passed so freely his way. Reclining back on an ocean of cushions, Jim is basking in the spirit of true affection at last.

Arthur has negotiated with Professor Mistry to do some work for him. Paul, a qualified electrician, joins them. The three of them rewire the house from top to bottom, then redecorate it. Professor Mistry has given them something rare: his complete trust and approval. They do not want to let him down and are spurred on to do their very best. On his return from a business trip in India, he is delighted with the results. Encouraged, he continues to find them work – in the garden, cleaning and even helping out with the reports he prepares.

Gradually, like a river flowing towards the sea, Jim begins to rediscover some motivation for living. He steadily digs his way out of the pit that has trapped him for so long. For the first time in decades, some of the people who drift into his life are not using drugs. And so, with a mixture of anticipation and dread, he looks ahead to his thirtieth birthday. This will be a milestone.

Joseph McKenzie has never given up on Jim. He continues to write out his prescriptions, talks sense without being patronising, and insists that Jim has the strength in him to stop.

"I'm ready." Jim's announcement one day takes the two of them by surprise. Jim has longed for Joseph to take the initiative, but instead he has waited patiently for Jim to take responsibility for himself. Together they work out a reduction programme which will allow Jim to wean himself off gradually. Jim aims to be clear by his birthday.

At the beginning of July, he swallows his last prescription of Linctus. He dispenses with his Valium. That blazing summer is a new kind of hell, but Jim is determined to endure it. Professor Mistry steps in with a request that Jim strips and paints his fence; this concentrates Jim's mind wonderfully. At night, Arthur and Jim meet in the pub and Jim drinks until the edges of his pain are sufficiently blurred to allow him to sleep for an hour or two. The rest of the night, he is awake and terrified.

Slowly things improve. He starts to spend time with a new friend, Tina, and her little daughter. Tina has recently separated from her husband, John, who is a junkie. The two remain on speaking terms and the pressure on Jim to rejoin the drug scene is intense.

It is Christmas 1983. Professor Mistry departs for Switzerland. Arthur leaves for Alsace in France. Jim is left alone, house sitting for the Mistrys. Not a good move. He grows lonely and depressed and broods on the past.

For the first time, he seriously considers a rehabilitation centre in the south of England that Joseph McKenzie told him about. Maybe he is ready for it. Taking the plunge, he applies for a place. For the next few days, he is filled with a mixture of exhilaration at the possibility of a completely different direction and apprehension at taking a giant step that will require so much from him. Despite the conflict of emotions, he is buoyed up by his own determination.

John is finally caught by the Drug Squad and suddenly Jim is privy to all the back stabbing and paranoia that is part of a big raid. It sickens him.

The arrival of the letter from Alpha House is timely. It says that

Jim has been accepted.

He wishes he could tell his friends, the much-loved Arthur among them, but he cannot let them know because he cannot run the risk of them talking him out of it. The last time they are together, Arthur, high on dope, catches Jim's eye and raises a drunken salute to him. Jim would give anything to rescue them but they would be deaf to his wildest appeals. When he leaves his buddies, tears fill his eyes. Will he see them again?

Three days after Easter, Jim takes the train to England, bound for a house full of strangers in a bid to scrape back his life. May God go with him.

CHAPTER 16

Here he is! The door opens and in he walks. Sitting down in front of the interview panel, Jim smiles nervously, eyes darting from side to side as he speaks. He lets them take the lead.

"Tell us a little bit about yourself," begins the first interviewer.

Jim clears his throat. "I was born in Glasgow. I had quite a poor upbringing... hated it where we lived. I used to look around at the other kids and think, I don't want to end up here. I studied hard, got to the grammar school. My dad died when I was eleven, which was really hard. Then my mother remarried. He used to take Dicanol, my stepfather. I started on it when I was 15. Dicanol and Mandrax."

Jim's eyes are scanning the room, as he speaks, as if he is being held captive, as if he is, even now, eyeing up possible escape routes. Perhaps he will cause a diversion and vanish suddenly through a window or a skylight?

"What are you hoping to achieve on the programme?"

"I want to get off drugs. I realise I am heading for prison or death. I can't stay doing what I'm doing."

Honest, at least. He searches their faces, his neck twitching nervously. Is he giving them what they are looking for? Jim is not terribly experienced at pleasing an audience. His last interview with the Post Office was not a resounding success.

Jim is not comfortable under questioning. More often than not it has been the police who have wanted to interrogate him and you have to be careful with them because they do not play by the Queensbury rules. They have stopped and searched him on the street and found gear even Jim himself knew he was not carrying.

"Balance of probabilities," one of them cheerily confided in him. Had it been any other day, Jim might indeed have been carrying, but that particular day, he was not. Is this justice? A fair cop? The police after all, can't afford to sit around and wait until they strike lucky, can they? What state would the world be in? So Jim cannot allow himself the luxury of confiding. Deeply painful issues he attempts to skirt over, but for once he is in the uncomfortable position of fooling no one.

"You do realise that once you're into the programme, you will attend encounter groups? You will be expected to participate fully in them. Is that something you're prepared to do, Jim?"

There is only one right answer.

"It's not something that comes easily, but I'm willing to give it a go."

They conclude with a handshake and a hug. Jim is uncomfortable, out of his depth, wondering what he has got himself into.

Jim knows no one here in England. He has left Scotland behind to come and live in a community of strangers on the South Coast. He is forbidden all contact with the outside world, his former friends, associates, even his own family. His mother is permitted to write to him only once he has completed six months of the programme. Alpha House is extremely strict in how they conduct business and for very good reason. Once someone embarks on the programme it has to be 100% commitment on both sides for the candidate to have any chance of successfully tackling their addiction. Absolutely no going back. A painful family dynamic, a disastrous love affair, an old contact sought out in a moment of weakness could all spell the end of recovery.

Jim gets up at 6 a.m. He scrubs the stone floors of the kitchen with a hand brush and a bowl of hot soapy water. It is demeaning, back breaking, soul-destroying work. It is constant, all day, apart from brief meal breaks. It is a regime that even prison will not institute and is designed to achieve two things: to break an individual's daily pattern of behaviour and to take away all spare time in which to think about drugs. Alpha House knows that most addicts will do anything to prevent themselves from engaging with difficult and painful emotions. To open the floodgates too far, too soon, would provoke agonising pain for many of their clients, so they occupy their bodies in constant, unending physical activity until they are bone exhausted and collapse into bed, grateful for eight hours of mind-numbing sleep.

A barely perceptible form enters from the darkness of the doorway and takes a seat. Jim is unwell. Tired and grey. Far from the thin, nervous, agile man who first entered Alpha House. He has wrestled a few demons by now. He is beginning to touch the edges of the vast challenge that lies ahead of him.

"How do you feel you've been getting on?" He is asked.

"I'm finding it all a bit weird. I mean, being in a house full of people I don't know, well, it is a bit strange. I don't think anyone would deny that."

Indeed they don't. They pause, leaving a measure of silence to see if he will expand on his feelings, but he rejects the opportunity. His arms are protecting his body in an embrace. His eyes are downcast, heavy with sadness.

"You are at the stage now, Jim, where many of your painful feelings are starting to surface. I notice that you have been very cynical about your peers. You seem highly critical of other people's behaviour – how selfish you think they are."

Jim considers this a moment.

"I can be cynical," he admits at last. "But I do believe I've got a lot to give. It's just that... I've felt let down by other people in the past."

"Do you ever think that this attitude might be preventing you from showing what you're capable of... for example, how dynamic you can be?"

Jim's breathing is shallow. His is struggling with the effort not to cry.

"I've had a lot put on me in the past by other people. I was always told I was in the wrong, that it was bad to cry, that I was different to everybody else." He attempts to navigate his way across the terrifying tightrope of his raw emotions.

They know, of course. That is exactly what they are attempting to do; carefully put him in touch with his pain.

"I feel a bit tense," he admits at last. It is a veiled cry for help.

A new session. It begins with greater clarity.

"You know, I hear a lot of this attitude. 'Poor Jim McPhail.' Well, it might work in the outside world but it won't wash in here."

Stuart is interviewing him now, pushing all Jim's buttons at once. He has alighted on the red hot topic of rejection.

"I'm really upset right now." Jim is sobbing uncontrollably. The boy, trapped years ago in his body, and so roundly ignored, is making a bid for freedom at last.

"You know, Jim," Stuart adds, kindly, "plenty of people in here have a lot of time for you. They really like you – if you'll let them. I for one really like you, Jim."

Jim glances upward. His ears are hearing unexpected music. Not everyone has given up on him. If they don't give up on him, there is every chance he may not have to give up on himself.

Here, like at home, he gravitates naturally towards making relationships with women. He has always been comfortable in female company.

At the next interview, Dave confronts Jim unexpectedly. "How does it feel to be labelled the womaniser of Alpha House?"

"Well, I've always liked women. I get on well with them." Jim is defensive, dismissive of the suggestion that this is a problem area.

"It certainly is an issue with you, Jim." Dave refuses to let him off the hook.

"In encounter groups, you are swift enough to confront any man you consider to be behaving badly. When it comes to the women, though, it's more of a case of smiling and being nice and letting them away with it, wouldn't you agree?"

Jim is honest enough to agree this is true.

The staff at Alpha are concerned. They know how swiftly entering the wrong relationship could derail all the progress Jim has made. There are hints that he is already on this path but he is refusing to admit it.

The further into the programme he goes, the less inclined they are, it seems, to give him the benefit of the doubt. Not that he is demanding special treatment, you understand. It's just that he is not used to such close scrutiny. The intense interest in his day to day life is startling and difficult for him.

He thought he could throw them off the scent, like a hunt saboteur diverting the hounds with aniseed but now he realises that once he has completed his work here, a different man entirely will emerge from his former shadow, so why upset the process?

"I believe I can achieve something great," he announces firmly to them. "Before, my life was lacking direction, but now, I believe in myself."

There is, within him, an indefinable wildness. Whether it is the legacy of his past, or part of his own nature, who can tell? The thin sculpted cheekbones and his black-brown hair define him as clearly as his emerging integrity. He wears a red shirt and his black trousers are pressed neatly as a knife edge. His huge long lashes and clear honest eyes defy you to disagree with his opinion. He maintains full eye contact throughout this, his final interview. He reveals a shining light deep within those dancing dark eyes, compelling you to watch him, daring you to doubt his charisma.

"What do you believe in, Jim McPhail?"

It is a highly charged question. "Well, I believe in myself, if that's what you mean!"

"Have you ever considered taking up the cloth?"

Jim smiles and shakes his head.

"Have you ever read Camus? The Outsider?"

He laughs. "God, no! I'm quite capable of getting myself depressed without artificial aids!" He grins reflectively. "I know you think I'm dour, but really, I laugh a lot now, I do. I've changed more than I ever thought possible. I'm happier now. I have belief in myself!"

It shows. Gesturing with his big hands as he talks, he eagerly announces his plans to them. He will get a job and a place to live. He doesn't know what else will happen, but he has optimism now, and hope that the future will be good.

He has the courage of his convictions. He is a man at the helm of his own ship, steering his way to his destiny, whatever forces might get in his way.

"Do you have any criticism of the way we run things here?" Stuart, as ever, demands brutal honesty of Jim.

"You know," Jim admits, at last, "the staff here are quite defensive of criticism. There are times when you're almost as bad at listening as I am!"

Stuart laughs, good naturedly, taking it on board in the spirit in which it was humbly offered. He has witnessed a vast change in Jim. Whoever thought to challenge Jim before Alpha did? Whoever loved him that much?

They rise and, one by one, they shake Jim's hand and hug him warmly to them.

PART 3

CHAPTER 17

I am Jim's future wife. I do not have a name yet. My parents cannot agree on one. I was planned and conceived in 1967, to celebrate my mother and father's wedding anniversary, but how could anyone plan me? They had no idea who I would be.

I spend the spring of 1968 riding around in my mother's womb, loved and gently talked to. I am a commuter on the journey to birth, hanging on upside down for dear life, puzzled by the topsy-turvy world I inhabit, full of warmth and pulsing heartbeats.

What have I let myself in for? I yell at the world on arrival, outraged at being deposited in the middle of my mother's bed at home, the one with dark blue flowers scattered across the bedspread. The bedroom overlooks the back garden, where the sun is out already. No time for any fuss. My mother promptly holds me and feeds me, and less than an hour later, she is up, making breakfast for everybody. I have so much black hair that my mother cuts it on the day I am born. A legacy of my Irish ancestry, on my father's side; that and my porcelain skin.

I survey the shapes around me. Faces that loom large and then mysteriously vanish. Swirling lampshades and ceilings for which I have no names yet. They merge seamlessly into one. I cannot make sense of any of it.

That's enough for one day, I think, firmly closing my eyes and jetting off back to sleep. Enclosed in my mother's arms, safe and warm, I am almost convinced I am back in the womb. You don't want to overdo things. Not on your first day.

I do not give up crying for anyone.

"God, I wish you'd give it a rest! You've been going on for hours! The neighbours will be ringing the NSPCC soon," exclaims my mother, half amused, half exasperated. "Whatever is it? I've fed you, changed you, held you. What's the matter now?"

I can't enlighten her. I hardly know myself.

"How is my little Kerry?" enquires my dad tenderly, peering into my cot.

"You mean Louise, I take it?" My mother stubbornly corrects him.

My father wins. My birth certificate confirms my name as Kerry. For the rest of her life, my mother calls me Louise. Or Lou, for short.

I am a late starter. I cannot stand up or walk for the first three years of my life. Instead I shuffle everywhere on my bottom and eat too many biscuits.

I have the gift of the gab though. I can talk the talk, even if I have yet to master the walk.

"I had to carry you all round Bournemouth in the rain last Saturday," my father moans, grudgingly, lifting me skywards for a cuddle. "My back's never been the same since."

In spite of his jibes, I am his favourite girl. I am his only daughter.

Frequently he sneaks home to mum and me at lunchtime. He eats his boiled egg and winks at me, then turns the empty shell upside down, distracting me momentarily and replaces it with a brand new egg while I am not looking. Tapping the top, he expresses delight at having had a rare two-sided egg for his lunch.

*

I am three years old and a big girl now. I never go anywhere without my posse in tow. Boo Boo, Pandy, Humpty Dumpty. Humpty Dumpty sits on inadequate stalk-thin legs, his ample green trousers dotted with pink and orange flowers that cover his huge waist. He looks mildly depressed. I can't say that I blame him. He had a tough time of it, falling off that wall. All the king's horses and all the king's men let Humpty down big time. It's no wonder he's got trust issues.

Boo Boo is amiable enough. He is a pale blue and white bear that my nan bought for my brother and he duly donated to me. Pandy is really his too. He is just on loan today. My mother says we must put him straight back on Andy's bed when we get home again, in case he notices he is missing.

I hastily convene a conference in the back of my mother's Hillman Imp while she drives us to nursery school. The consensus is that we would rather be going to the park. I gather up my toys determinedly and race along the path to nursery with them in my arms.

Do you remember your first day at nursery?" My mother asks. "You cried your eyes out when I took you in. It wouldn't have been so bad but I worked there too!"

There is a yellow plastic trainer seat in the bathroom here, because some of the children are still such babies that they haven't even learnt how to sit on the toilet properly.

I sit on a wooden chair in a line, in among thirty other kids. We eat finger biscuits that taste of corrugated cardboard and drink milk in silver topped bottles with a straw. I am a solitary soul, primly colouring in the grass on my picture sheet. Everyone is busy admiring Karen Clarke's grass because it is completely smooth and she hasn't gone over the lines, but that's rubbish. Real life shows you that grass is all different lengths, like mine is. You can't neaten everything up, just because it suits you.

I retreat into my books whenever I get the chance. I love Rumplestiltskin but hate Sleeping Beauty who is a sissie. If I can count up to fifteen in one go, I can win a book that will teach me how to count up to fifteen all over again. I fix my eyes firmly on the wall opposite. A clock is hanging there but I cannot tell what the time is yet.

"1, 2, 3,"

JAMES WITH A SILENT C

Simon, sitting cross legged on the rug beside me, made it as far as fourteen on his go. That's the highest anyone has ever managed. I reckon he must have had help.

"4, 5, 6,"

I think of my daddy and how proud he will be of me.

"7, 8, 9,"

My mother has paused from wiping faces and is watching me, transfixed.

"10, 11, 12,"

I can almost reach out and touch it. The counting book is called Dylan and the Magic Roundabout. Dylan is the rabbit and he is my favourite.

"13, 14, 15!"

A leap of faith! A triumph! They are clapping me.

Beaming, I lean forward and Mrs. Osmond presents me with the book. Dylan the Rabbit peers languidly back at me from the front cover as he strums his guitar.

I race outside, in my red rain mac, clutching the book to me, more excited than I have ever been about anything.

"Look! Look! I won!" I chatter excitedly to my mother.

"Yes, you did!" She smiles proudly, my posse of toys in her arms. Humpty Dumpty hangs from beneath her elbow, eyeing the pavement apprehensively.

We go back home and start the housework. I don't think anyone appreciates how hard Mum and I work to keep the house looking nice. It isn't easy. There are only so many hours in the day.

106

CHAPTER 18

Saturday mornings I like to make a cardboard horse if Dad is not too busy to help me. We take a huge cardboard presentation stand which came from his work and which he keeps in the garage, and we bring it indoors. We fold it in half, which makes the horse's body. Then we add a cardboard head, with eyes and ears, and I make it a woolly mane. I spend ages drawing a saddle on it, and give it a woolly tail. Then all that is left is to name it Snowdrop and feed it sugar cubes before I ride it down the hall and back.

If my Wendy House is up, I disappear inside and pretend it is the stables. I like to do high jumps over the poles of the frame before the cover goes on. If someone is over, I have to pretend to keep house and offer them tea in a plastic cup. But I do not like keeping house.

No one appreciates a woman's work. My brother and I are fed up with having to lift our legs up on the settee for Mum to hoover underneath. Plus, if we are trying to listen to TV, the hoover drowns the sound out. Even my Dad gets irritated by it.

"Can't you leave that til Monday, Carol? Come and sit down," he pipes up.

But my mother gets annoyed and says that by Monday it will need doing again. She says it's easy for Dad. He can just get up and get into the car, ready to go, but she has to check that the windows are shut and the oven is off and fetch the door keys.

My mother is afraid that the housework will never get done. Every day, as soon as my father has left the house, she sets to work with a vengeance, duster in one hand, hoover in the other. Emptying bins, cleaning the sink, clearing out the wardrobes and washing the nets. It is a frantic operation. If anyone from across the road pops in for a cup of tea, it sets her back hours. Only when it is all done does the tyranny recede.

"It isn't all as instant as your father likes to think!" She tells me. I think it would be better if she told my father this and tell her so, but she cuffs my ear and tells me not to be so cheeky.

*

On long car journeys, I am allowed a paper bag of things to eat because it keeps me quiet. I peer inside hopefully and count two Ritz crackers, an iced ring party biscuit and three jelly tots, two pink and one green. I sit munching thoughtfully until we reach the traffic lights.

"Lou, have you started your bag already?" Mum asks.

I have the decency to flush with embarrassment. My mother snorts with disbelief.

"John! She's only finished it already!"

I feel ashamed, briefly, like a horse caught with its head in a nosebag. Ritz crumbs tumble down my jersey. I am a tubby little girl who eats too much.

On holiday mornings, I like to watch Belle and Sebastian, which is in black and white. Belle is a huge dog and Sebastian is the little boy who befriends her. It is set in a foreign country where it snows all the time and actually settles. You have to go to school and back on skis and I would like to live there. Instead I content myself with roller skating on the gravel outside all afternoon, nearly colliding with my brother on his scooter. We launch into a fight to settle the matter until my mother arrives on the scene and announces, "I'll bang both your heads together. Now get indoors, the pair of you!"

*

Later, when I am in my bath, I stare at the knotted swirls of wood on the back of the door and conjure up pictures in my mind's eye.

Gnarled dwarfs carry treasure on their backs and dragon kings guard their caves, while mermaids swim in the nearby seas. A beautiful princess is crying in a tower with no one to rescue her.

"Have you fallen asleep in there?" My mother asks, knocking on the door.

I assure her, indignantly, I have not , drying myself with a towel and changing into my pyjamas before she catches up with me.

A big black shadow hangs over the back of my bedroom door every night, like a crow, waiting to pounce on me. Mum shooed it away once, by putting the hall light on and showing me that it wasn't real, but the second she returned to bed it came back again.

One night I dream my daddy has died. I wake up with tears streaming down my face and call to mum because I am so sad.

"He's not dead, love. He's right here! Look!"

"Hello Tulip. I'm OK," he says reassuringly, wrapped in his dark paisley dressing gown. He cuddles me to show me he is real. I go back to sleep.

CHAPTER 19

"There are children in Africa who would be glad of what you've left on your plate!" My mother chides.

I think, selfishly, that they are welcome to my beef casserole because it is full of gristle and nothing on earth will persuade me to swallow it. I spit it out surreptitiously and hide it in my hankie, then up my sleeve, so that my mother doesn't find out.

I always have room for jam rolled pudding.

"Not an end piece, please!" I plead. I like the middle best.

Sometimes I have custard on it too, but not tonight. I like to eat things dry, like my Dad does. Except that I like butter on my toast in the mornings, whereas he likes his bread without. Mum says that is how they eat it in prison and that he could at least put a bit of dripping on it, so he does, to please her.

Mum says, "He doesn't know what he's eating, half the time, your father." She says this is because he doesn't have any taste buds like the rest of us. And he can eat amazingly hot things and not mind. He doesn't have to wait for his soup to cool down by blowing on it, like I do. Mum says Dad hasn't got his own teeth; that's why he doesn't notice if things are hot or what they taste of. Sometimes, when Mum is not looking, Dad will drop his front set of teeth down to make me laugh. If we have a box of chocolates and there is one that nobody likes, like a lemon cream, we give it to Dad to eat because he doesn't mind.

"That's all right," he says, mildly. "You can all laugh, but at least I keep you all happy!"

JAMES WITH A SILENT C

My mum thinks I am the image of my Irish nan, who is called her 'mother in law.' I am glad because I think my nan is beautiful with her really dark hair with no grey in it at all even though she is ever so old having been alive for fifty years. Her eyes twinkle mischievously. My Irish nan thinks I am beautiful even though I have no front teeth and look like a witch.

My mother always adds a swift disclaimer, "She doesn't look like either of us, though, does she?" Then she laughs and looks at my father.

Whenever Nan comes to see us, we rush along the train platform to greet her, my brother and I, clamouring with excitement because she has come all the way from London for Sunday tea and there is a trifle and we have done drawings too. She gets off the train, and holds my hand, which makes me feel very special because everyone sees us as we walk towards Dad's car. He goes round to the passenger door and helps her in, exactly like she is a film star. In the big bag she is carrying are presents for me and my brother. Mine is a sausage dog who barks and wags his tail and has a little chain lead and a yellow mouth and a red tongue. I take him for walks across the carpet and Sooty the cat is very jealous of him and attacks him if she gets the chance, so we have to switch him off and make a big fuss of her until she settles down to sleep.

It is very exciting to talk to Nan because she lives in London and that is the centre of the world. There are theatres there and she says she will take me one day when I am bigger and come up to stay with her. I cannot wait. I am not a baby, but Nan likes to cuddle me and calls me her baby and pretends to rock me for a joke.

My mum lays the tea things out on the coffee table, with little doilies because this is a special occasion.

Nan says, "Ooh, look! Trifle!" and "Aren't we posh!" and clasps her hands together delightedly, but my mum says she is 'making comments' and she bickers with my dad about it afterwards.

The afternoon is all magical, like Christmas, and I am allowed to wave Nan off from the doorstep and to run after the car, waving, but I am not allowed to go to the train station to see her off because I am too little and have to go to bed. My brother goes, because he is older than me. It is not fair, because I really love my nan, but I get into my bath, albeit in a huff. Then, suddenly, I do not mind because I have a new pink sponge to play with.

*

Afterwards, we sit down together on the settee, Mum and I, and she reads aloud, one arm around me and the other balancing the book. I don't go much for Cinderella. I vastly prefer the Ugly Sisters, shoving their ill-fitting feet into the glass slipper in a bid to win the Prince's affections. My mother says there is too much of the martyr in Cinders, which means she won't stand up for herself properly. She doesn't strike me as the kind of girl who climbs trees or goes poking about in muddy streams. If we'd gone out to play in the woods together, she'd have been worrying about messing up her pink ball gown the whole time.

Tucked up next to Mum, leaning in close to her as she reads, I feel warm and safe in the knitted argyle jumper she has made me. My mother doesn't believe in Cinderella either, though sometimes I think she would have liked to. Real life intrudes rather too often with its grocery bills and Green Shield stamps and HP.

I have a huge illustrated Bible and love reading that God saw fit to curse the Egyptians with twelve plagues. I feel sorry for them, balancing their beautiful head dresses and squelching frogs underfoot. How did they endure a plague of locusts? That summer, we have a plague of our own. Caterpillars invade the lawn until it is a moving carpet. Everywhere you look they are squirming, writhing and chewing. The neighbours come from across the road to compare notes with us. All the mums shake their heads in dismay. I wonder what the residents of Eglantine Walk have done to incur the wrath of God? It doesn't seem to take much. Mum tells me that a plague of locusts can eat up a single field in a day. I start watching the sky warily. They normally approach, she says, like an oncoming cloud, blocking out the sun in flight. You can't be too careful, it seems.

CHAPTER 20

I have made a den from an old sheet of corrugated iron propped up between the fence and the wall. I sit here watching a brown spider with a white cross on its back spinning a web across the branches of the tree. Reaching up, I prod the centre of its web with a tiny bit of leaf and watch the spider tear along its gossamer threads in the belief it has caught a fly.

Dad calls to me from the back door, ready to go out. Every Sunday morning we walk together for miles through the woods. We share a bag of Sharpe's toffees and talk about dinosaurs and moon landings. All the time I am glowing with pride because evidently my father is the most intelligent man in the world. I tell him so and he laughs and says it is a fine thing his genius is being recognised at last.

A boy was lost in the sewerage tunnel that runs through the woods and no one ever saw him again. I know, because Helen at school told me. Sometimes people hear his ghostly cries. Once, Helen and I banged the side of the pipe and hollered to him, "Aaaannnyyooonneee in there?" But we took fright at our own echoes and ran off from the trickling stream of water that seeped out of the tunnel. I tell Dad about it, but he just smiles and says he doesn't think it is true about the lost boy. All the same, you must be careful, because it is a dangerous thing to go wandering about near tunnels, he says.

The trees form a canopy overhead in the woods. You can't see the sky any more, it is so dense with leaves. You can hear the branches twitch and snap with bird's feet as they forage for insects. I put my hand through the crook of Dad's arm and am relieved when we come out in the daylight again.

We spot a tiny, fluffy brown owl perched on a branch, watching us in broad daylight. Once I found a skeleton of a bird's head in the woods which I have kept in a box at home ever since. It is amazingly delicate, bleached white and intricate. I take it out to look at sometimes, but Mum always makes me wash my hands afterwards because she says it is dirty.

On we go, Dad and I, but today the ground becomes so muddy that we are forced to walk along by the fence for the last half mile. They are digging to make way for the motorway and where will all the animals live then?

"We got a bit muddy," Dad talks Mum round for me afterwards so that we don't get into trouble. He tells her he loves her and calls her Treasure. Mum snorts derisively and tells him, "On your bike," but she gives him extra roasties, just the same.

That night, when it is properly dark, Dad and I go outside and gaze up at the stars. He is pleased that I can now point out the Plough and Little Bear.

"It's incredible to think that what you are looking at now is how the stars looked millions of years ago," he says.

I put my hand in his warmed gloved hand and he squeezes it tightly. If you were standing on one of those stars tonight, gazing back down at the earth, you would see cavemen and woolly mammoths. There would be no schools to go to and no offices to work in. We stand for a moment, thinking about what a wonderful world it must have been. Then we grin at each other and go indoors because Coronation Street is about to start.

*

In the summer you can start a fire with a magnifying glass, even a tiny one that you have saved out of a Christmas cracker, like I have. My brother is expert at getting leaves to smoke in the garden, before stopping just in time and stamping them out. If you look into the glass while the sun is reflected in it, you will never be able to see again.

I give up. Everything is deemed too dangerous. I go and look at my caterpillars in their bright green leathery jackets, their pale blue underbellies stretched to bursting. They lie fat and dreaming in their jam jar prison. They do not even have the energy to eat the leaves I have shoved in alongside them.

"Don't forget you've got the dentist this afternoon," Mum calls out the back door.

Abandoning my caterpillars, I race indoors. I want a drink before I brush my teeth. Gulping down a Ribena, I realise how thirsty I am and promptly refill my glass with water.

"Make sure you go to the loo first, before we leave," cautions Mum.

We set off. If I am well-behaved in the dentist's chair, I am allowed a packet of coloured sticky shapes afterwards from the newsagents.

"Open wide," grins Mr. La Fosse. He has a picture of Africa on the ceiling and I gaze up anxiously into a lion's roaring mouth. I shut my eyes and concentrate on my sticky shapes instead.

Afterwards we may eat again because we do not need to go to the dentists for another whole year. My brother and I eat an iced bun each from the bakery while we sit on the scorching hot plastic seats in the back of my mother's car.

I skip up the path to the back door, pausing to check on my caterpillars. A terrible sight meets my eyes. They are all shrivelled and dark and have fallen off their leaves.

"Oh, Lou," my mother despairs. "You've left them out in the sun, poor things. They've died in the heat."

I throw my head into my hands and sob. I have killed them. I am a murderer and it is all my fault because I forgot to leave them in the shade. They didn't deserve such a terrible end and have to be thrown out with the rubbish. I sit indoors and put the sticky shapes out across the kitchen table so that I can look at them properly. I always like the yellow square best, but not today because I do not deserve my favourite after what has happened.

There is going to be a thunderstorm tonight. The air is taut with electricity and the clouds are holding their breath. Outside, after dinner, we watch the ants fly up out of their nests onto the lawn. The air is thick with them. They land on our T-shirts and bare arms. Ants carrying eggs on their backs swarm frantically up from the cracks in the paving, restless and agitated, before disappearing down new holes. An enormous thunderclap booms overhead and we all cheer because it has been so hot that, for seven days now, we have had to eat giant purple salt tablets to combat the heat.

I am desperate to feel the rain on my skin. I want to shampoo my hair in it, out of doors, but I am scared of being outside in a storm. I race back inside and Mum turns the TV set off so that the house does not catch fire.

Dad is not home yet. He is driving back from Nottingham and it takes him many hours. I am afraid for him, and try to remember if it is good or bad to have rubber tyres on your car in a thunderstorm.

Mum says that the thunder is just the noise of God rearranging his furniture and that it is nothing to be afraid of. All the same, when the streaks of lightening illuminate the room, she jumps.

Eventually the storm passes over and I go to bed.

Dad is home safe at last. He pops his head around my bedroom door, still in his work suit.

"Night night, Tulip," he says gently.

"Night night, Dad," I reply.

Outside the thunder rumbles distantly. The storm is quite far away now. You can tell by counting in between the booms of thunder and the flashes of lightening. Every second is a mile in distance.

CHAPTER 21

I am Jim's future wife. Right now though, I am busy doing hand stands on the lawn at home. You can't blame me. I am only nine. I can walk upside down on my hands, too, if you dare me. I have a photograph my father took in which my best friend and I are holding hands and leaping high in the air. My hair is skywards. Nothing is impossible to us. We defy gravity momentarily. We are flying through life.

I have not met Jim yet. We are fourteen years away from setting eyes on each other. But he is, nevertheless, inscribed indelibly on my heart. He is the man I will one day fall in love with. When I am pretending to be a bride, walking up the garden path towards a make believe altar, with a net curtain concealing my face, it is Jim that I am walking towards. He is imprinted on my soul. The map of my life leads me inexorably towards him.

For now, though, I am more interested in Charles Darwin and beetles. I have an insatiable curiosity for the natural world.

I am watching a butterfly emerge from its chrysalis. I kept a caterpillar in a jar all summer and fed it on leaves. In August, it died, or I thought it had. It stopped moving and a skein of silk grew around it and it disappeared inside a sticky brown case. I kept tapping experimentally at it with my finger. Just now, I crouched low on the grass and noticed that the top part of it was moving. Antennae were poking out of it, so I called Mum over to watch. We were dead excited. An entire red admiral butterfly emerged from the cocoon. It was amazing, all scarlet, black and white, as if an artist had painted it by hand. It perched on the side of the jar, drying its wings. Then it took off and fluttered around the garden and over the top of the fence. We never saw it again.

People think they only live for a day, butterflies, but it isn't true. Sometimes they make it through the winter even, if they can find shelter in an attic.

Some people believe in God. Other people think there is only what you can see in front of your eyes. Me? I think that what you can see is plenty of proof there is God. Take the diamond sparkles of dew hanging silently from the spiders' cobwebs that criss-cross the rose bushes. Or the sun, sinking into a vast rose-gold bath against a backdrop of autumnal sky. We stand in the hay-den in the woods, after school, watching it set and I think, *there* is God, right in the centre of it.

Then there is my father who lifts me up, safe and warm and spins me around in his arms until I am nearly sick with laughing. It is Friday and there is no work tomorrow so he is doubly happy. The stars left behind in the night sky keep watch over us, twinkling with the promise of eternity.

I do not for a minute think God is angry with any of us, even if Mr. Jones our Head Teacher does. When he booms on about hell and damnation in assembly, I switch off. It is not his fault he does not know God like I do. Mr. Jones clearly has no woods to walk in.

Now I am nine, I am suspicious of the fact there are many more photographs of my brother as a baby than there are of me.

"Was I an ugly baby, Mum?" I enquire one day.

"No, you were both lovely babies, you and your brother. People used to stop me in the street to admire you!" Beams my mother with pride.

Deeply unsatisfied, I pursue the matter with my father.

"Tell me the truth. Was I adopted?"

I brace myself for his answer.

"Don't be daft! Besides, who would have chosen you?" He grins, delightedly.

My mother doesn't appreciate wasting time. Her hands are never idle, whether she is dusting, hovering or cooking. In the evenings she knits and sews. Now and then, she makes me little toys, like the trio of tiny purple kittens I found in my dressing gown pocket one night time.

I never doubt that I am loved. The comfort and reassurance of her presence in the old green chair beside my bed at night demonstrates how much she cares. The way she lets me sit on an upturned flower pot in the garden, nattering endlessly to her while she turns the soil with a fork lets me know how close we are.

What does my mother think about love?

She tells me that she remembers pushing me in my pram one day and colliding with a work mate from long ago.

"Carol, you remember Alan, don't you?" The woman breezed breathlessly with gossip on her lips.

My mother played dumb for a moment, but her heart was racing. "Alan Morris? Course you do!"

She bit into her lip, desperate to know.

"He died, you know. Last year. They found him in his flat in London. Terrible shame. They say he used to drink. He was very fond of you, you know."

The woman's face changed from one of friendly openness to terrible intrusion.

"They said he still had your photograph in his wallet when they found him. Imagine, Carol. All those years and he was still thinking of you."

My mother makes her excuses and leaves. The woman shrugs and raises her eyebrows. What has she done wrong? Not her fault he died, is it? She totters along the road on her high heels, her mind already elsewhere.

My mother pushes the pram blindly ahead of her. But she cannot see through her tears.

"I thought I loved him once," she admits. "A long time ago."

I don't know what to say.

"He wanted us to live together, but I wanted to get married. He was a lot older than me. I think he knew it would be unfair to marry me. He knew it couldn't last, not really. I was too young."

"But you loved him?" I am quietly devastated for her.

"I gave him an ultimatum. I told him I would waste three years of my life on him, then I would walk away if we weren't engaged by then."

"And…?"

"Three years came and went. So I finished it." Her face contorts briefly at the memory.

"I'd just started dating your father. He had proposed to me. Then the very next day, Alan rang me, wanting to meet. I went to the pub to see him and he proposed to me too."

"Oh my God, Mum! What did you do?"

"I said 'No' of course."

"But you loved him."

"I loved your father." She corrects me, decisively. "I made the right choice."

I reach forward and throw my arms around her neck.

"You know, Mum, Alan might have turned out to be a terrible man, whereas Daddy really does love us all. So I think it was the right decision too."

My mother nods and says that sounds very sensible to her.

"Anyway," she continues smiling. "Your father needs me. He wouldn't even eat properly if I didn't make him."

I thought long and hard about love. It didn't strike me that it should have anything to do with pain or loss.

That night I watch my father tucking into his bangers and mash, oblivious to the bomb that once exploded in my mother's life. He winks at me and I beam back at him and think, smugly, that she definitely made the right choice.

It never once occurs to me I would not even be here had she not done so.

CHAPTER 22

I have lost the unshakeable faith I once had in Father Christmas. I begin to suspect subterfuge.

It starts with the Generation Game Christmas Eve Special. We sit entranced in the lounge, watching the contestants at the conveyer belt on TV. Mum is on the settee, nursing a glass of sherry with my brother at her side. Dad is in his armchair and I am kneeling on the floor one minute, up dancing around the next.

"How many can you remember as you play along at home?" Asks Bruce Forsyth.

"The toaster, the cruet set, the cuddly toy," I begin chanting.

The terrible row that breaks out on Christmas Eve blows up out of nowhere. My mother and father spill out into the hall, yelling at each other. Then Mum dissolves into tears of rage and slams the door in Dad's face.

We creep silently to bed, my brother and I.

The next day, all is well. My mother and father have plastered on their smiles. No cracks appear anywhere in our Christmas. I tuck into my turkey, relieved, one eye on the remaining crackers on the table. I have spent the last ten days peering expectantly up the cardboard tubes trying to establish what is inside them. I would like a tin whistle and a red hat.

In the night, I dream of aeroplanes flying overhead and wake to discover Sooty, my pet cat, perched beside me, purring in my ear. Then I hear raised voices in the kitchen. My heart sinks and I turn over on my pillow to drown them out.

Boxing Day morning, I am lost in a fantasy, drawn into the rare, magical world of the Snow Queen.

It is snowing outside. I am caught between my desperate desire to watch the TV adaptation and my need to see the snow. I tip my head under the net curtains, wearing them like a bridal veil while keeping an ear out for the TV. Outside, snowflakes are falling silently and the Snow Queen is in their midst, where the cloud is thickest. At midnight she will fly through the streets and look in at the windows, then the ice on the panes will freeze into strange and wonderful shapes, like flowers. She is alive, but made of ice. Her eyes flash like two clear stars, but there is neither peace nor rest in their glance.

I am pretending to be Gerda, the little girl in the story. The boy is called Kay. We love each other dearly, but Kay has been struck in the heart and in the eye with shards of a demonic broken mirror. He sees only ugliness everywhere. He has turned against everyone in his bitterness, and now he is gone. The Snow Queen has beckoned to him and ushered him far, far away. He has left his friends behind and no one is sure what has become of him. I am transfixed. The story holds my rapt attention. Gerda must find him. Only she has the power to redeem him from the evil clutches of the mirror.

Later I turn off the TV, the story still racing through my imagination. Wrapping up warmly, I set off for the woods to join my friend Helen and her family. The pond where we meet is covered in ice and they are already skating confidently around the centre. I set out across the ice, just like Gerda does in the story, in search of Kay, only I have no ice skates, just my wellingtons.

"Come on! It's great!" They urge me.

I have forgotten how to let go and trust. What once seemed certain is now cracking beneath my feet. I slip through the ice and begin to sink.

"Hold on! You're OK!"

Helen's older brother and sister fish me out. I retreat to the safety of the path that runs around the pond. My boots are full of ice-cold water and my legs are soaked. My jeans cling to me as I watch them all playing happy families, but I can't join them. My eyes are filled with tears, but it is not about the ice. Deep down I feel lonely. I wish I had a big family like Helen.

"That could have been really dangerous – I'm surprised at Helen's mother," admonishes Mum, drying my wet hair with a towel and making me change my socks. I am drinking hot Bovril in a mug. She is wrong. It wasn't dangerous. I was a coward. Hot tears run down my face, mingling with my drink on my tongue.

"Shh. You've had a bit of a shock, that's all." She smoothes my hair and sets about peeling the carrots.

"Here," she hands me a sliver of raw carrot and I eat it, consoled temporarily.

"Mum," I pause. "Do you still love Dad?"

"Of course! He's all right. He's just your father," she laughs, as if wondering why I am asking.

In my dreams that night, I skate perfectly across the ice towards Kay. I am Gerda. He catches hold of me and spins me round and around in his arms. We laugh and are happy together. I will never give up on him.

CHAPTER 23

It's all gone now. They built the motorway right through my beloved woodlands, three years after they started. There is nothing left of it now. Birds no longer sing in the overhanging branches of the oak trees. The little owl my father and I once saw is no more peering expectantly at us from the fence. Foxes that used to dart playfully about in the dusk must now content themselves with trawling through rubbish bins in back gardens. What became of us, the children whose laughter echoed through the woods? We too have moved on. We hang about in bus shelters, swaggering and pretending to be grown up. Helen and her family moved away last year and I haven't seen them since.

As for us? We are moving on too. Nothing stays the same forever, however much you wish it would.

Our new house is decorated throughout in magnolia paint and has the same light brown carpet running all the way through. There is no stone clad fireplace here, no shelf on which a steam train sits, no place for the china rabbit money box with his drum and drumsticks to play. Instead we have crystal wine glasses on display in a cabinet. The old sideboard, from which I sat and waved to my father, is gone. It was no longer in fashion.

The weeds in the new garden are as tall as my waist. My brother and I hack them down as a start to laying a lawn. Fat, grub-like caterpillars hang from their stalks. They repulse me. I no longer want to collect them in jam-jars. I do not believe they will ever become beautiful butterflies.

We are lucky, having a brand new house to live in.

I go out exploring on my own and wander through a farmer's field full of poppies. A sheepdog rushes towards me but passes on by, intent on other pursuits. Halfway up the hill, there is a sweet shop where a man sells chocolate rum truffles in a paper bag. I buy two ounces and he lets the scales slip over in my favour and doesn't charge me any extra.

Outside a bike skids to a halt beside me on the pavement.

"Hullo!" It is Ian, from school.

"All right!" I stiffen up, shyly.

"You just moved in?"

"Yep."

"My dad says your family must be snobs cos you live in a new house."

"Well, we're not," I object, hackles raised.

"Well, you are. You live in a snob's house," Ian declares stoutly again. "My dad says so."

He grins and speeds away from me.

All around us are unfinished houses. Skeletons of scaffolding and partly laid bricks. There are holes where the window panes have yet to be installed. My friend Ally and I climb up to pinch the pats of putty that the builders have left behind.

At night, when it is dark, lots of the neighbours go out looking for things they need for their own homes. No one admits to this in the daylight because everyone knows it is a secret.

I do not like my new school. I am on the sixth floor of a high rise comprehensive block. Everyone is mean to a girl called Cheryl because she does not fit in. You have to watch that Darren Taylor doesn't pinch your bum when you are going downstairs. He yanks my ponytail and I kick him hard where it hurts but he just laughs so I scowl at him instead.

I walk to school still, but now I take the radio instead of books.

As I pass under the subway, the traffic whizzes past me on its way to join the motorway. Everything I loved has been replaced by concrete; the grass, the trees, the hedgerows. Even the sky is no longer blue. A wicked witch cast a spell and made it forever winter and never summer and green things no longer flourish anywhere. The only wild animals I ever see now are already dead, by the side of the road. Squashed hedgehogs and ripped up foxes, thrown to the kerb. They should have been tottering under hedges and trotting across moonlit fields but now they never get the chance. An evil spell has turned them all to stone.

I no longer want to live here. I feel empty. I save up my pocket money and start skipping school. I catch the train up to London with my friend Ally and spend all day in the freezing cold outside the Top of the Pops studio. We watch the latest bands draw up in limousines and they wave to us through the windows. This is what passes for happiness now. I do not care if I get into trouble for it.

"You needn't think you're having any dinner tonight!" My mother yells at me.

I am starving, but my pride will not allow me to admit it. I slink off to bed early, too hungry to sleep. I lie staring at the walls, feeling bleak and despondent.

Only the thought of the bright lights keeps me going. The endless pulsating traffic of London with its crowded streets and smart black cabs. I will return there one day.

My mother says, "You know what your trouble is, don't you? You think too much."

She says that no one is really happy in this life but they just get on with it.

CHAPTER 24

Jim hasn't been home in over two years. Returning to Glasgow is a daunting, if exciting, prospect. He has missed his family. Imagine how he feels, stepping onto the platform of Glasgow Central Station to see his sister Beth waiting for him.

"God, Jim – you look so well. Come here!" She throws her arms around him and wells up instantly, barely able to believe this is the same man who left.

His mother is quietly pleased to see him. She has been drinking more in recent years. This is what he was most dreading. Hating the bottles, hidden under the sink, that were never alluded to. Margaret has lived alone since Davie perished in the fire. The good days ended a long time before. Here's to them, she thinks dolefully, raising her tea to her lips.

"It's good to see you, son," she nods, motioning for him to sit down on the settee beside her. She is glued to Take the High Road, and quickly fills him in on the progress of the characters. Beth raises an eyebrow mischievously over her head at him.

They couldn't stop it, any of them. He realises that now. Margaret could no more hold back the weight of history than King Canute could order back the sea. She is still wearing her pain. It is written in her eyes, her puzzled, hurting expression. Why me? Why my family? They are questions she asks over and over, without comfort or cessation. She has no words to offer Jim. She loves him in her own way and she is proud of him. He feels a sudden rush of tenderness towards her, and regrets that they will never be close.

"Arthur's doing all right too, you know," Beth gently nudges Jim.

"Is he?" His eyes light up. "Great, I'd love to see him."

But rumours of Arthur's recovery have been greatly exaggerated and Jim's heart sinks when he sees him in a café on the Great Western Road. Arthur swaggers over in his dark, floor length overcoat, totally stoned, with Paul in tow. Ghosts sauntering back into his life, even as their shared past recedes from him. Jim talks to them, tries to reason with them, but is forced to leave. He cannot bear the fact that Arthur is still stubbornly resistant to the need to get clean. Jim is gazing into a mirror image of his own past and it is one that nearly killed him.

Back in England, a furious row erupts between Jim and his new girlfriend. She has cheated on him in his absence. He faces the possibility of living alone and a sinking feeling in his abdomen almost convinces him he will not manage. But he recognises the feeling as grief churning up from his past, trying to conquer him in its grasp. Jim moves out of the accommodation he was sharing with his girl and into a bedsit. Beth has given him her old stereo which he installs. He enjoyed his trip home but he senses he needs to find a new home now. His own home. It's not much, this dingy little bedsit, and there are times when he finds it hard to keep going, but he won't let the walls close in on him. Never again will he sit alone and desolate with a needle in his arm.

Finally he understands for himself what the staff at Alpha House kept trying to tell him – that his dependence on drugs was the product of his past pain. With that knowledge, he trusts he will make it. He is determined. Maybe one day, he'll even find true love, he reasons, swirling a brandy glass in his hand and staring intently into the bottom of it to see if it reveals an answer.

*

I am Jim's future wife. I am trying to find my way around with an A-Z but it is a huge place. You don't realise until you are right in the middle of it. The easiest way is to follow the maps on the

Underground but of course you have to know where you are trying to get to first.

I ran away to London in the end. I did it properly. I waited until I finished school, I got a job, I got a transfer. This will be the start of everything.

Of course I have no idea that Jim, having left Alpha House behind, has chosen to settle in my native Southsea. If I did, do you think I would have ever left? He is wandering through my old haunts, propped at a bar, listening to the same bands, drinking in the same pubs. Never mind that. We weren't to know.

I will get the hang of this. I am aware that all around me pickpockets are waiting to pounce if I look like a tourist.

I stride confidently out into the traffic in the Strand, weaving my way in and out of the black cabs, ignoring the jammed horns of the irate drivers, scowling at any courier cyclists who have the audacity to cross my path and thanking God silently that I make it alive to the other side.

It is huge, living here. I squeeze myself with excitement every time I walk past the BBC at Bush House. I work directly opposite Somerset House and there is a tiny beautiful church in the centre of the traffic island.

There are eight of us on the first floor, and the security guards know me well enough now to give me the nod and say, "Good Morning, Madam" as I pass and it makes me feel really important when I am only a girl from Portsmouth.

I get into the carpeted elevator and think I am really someone. I just want to be a singer. When I go down to the basement, where the record files are kept, Paul the storeman lets me sing Witney Houston songs full tilt. I prefer Nina Simone's *I Put a Spell on You*, but Paul does not know that one. He says if he doesn't know the song, how can he tell if I'm any good or not?

He fancies Jo, a girl we work with, but she is married so he says he might as well forget about that mightn't he? Love doesn't always work out, does it?

At night I eat dinner with my flatmates. There are eight of us, but none of us ever washes up. The landlord despairs of us, and swaggers in, half-cut, and announces he is throwing everything into a black bin liner at midnight if it is not all cleared away by then.

The roof of the downstairs toilet fell in one day because it snowed so heavily and now you can see the clouds sail by when you are sitting on the loo. You have to remember to take a cardigan but it is worth it, because you might wait at least half an hour to get into the bathroom upstairs. I get up first, before anyone, and tiptoe down to use the roofless one.

I sing backing vocals in a recording studio in Kings Cross. The producer runs me home in his car in the early hours of the morning. I have to drink at least six cups of real coffee to stay awake long enough to do my day job, but it is worth it. One day I hope to be famous and a man will adore me and I will never have to worry about a thing.

Everything I knew from childhood has left me now, except the stories. Tattered, much loved paperbacks line the walls of my room. I return to them again and again, searching for a way back to my own personal Narnia.

I want to find true love. I have not found him yet, my man, but my heart yearns for him as surely as if he were here.

I lift a coffee cup to my lips. I am in Bloomsbury, in a cafe with my flatmate.

"This time next year, I will have married my soul mate," I predict confidently.

"Yeah, right." She is scornful. Maybe she doesn't believe in love. But I do.

All of London passes by the windows. I have only ever been on the periphery, I realise sadly.

I came here expecting to make the big time but only my heart knows how to sing. My voice stumbles over unfamiliar songs. I try in vain to find a place where I truly belong.

Where are you? I whisper, alone in the night, as my head touches the pillow.

Have you seen the one I love? I ask the moon, as he peers in through the glass. The sycamore tree outside keenly senses my loneliness and yields its leaves to the wind in response.

Will he ever come?

I cannot bear the thought of being alone forever. I draw the duvet close around me and sit up, waiting.

I perch on a bench in Soho Park Square and write a story. Perhaps it will come true. Tearing the paper up, I promptly deposit it in the bin. Tomorrow the man from the council will collect it and it will be as if it never existed.

When I am in love, I will no longer commune with the trees in autumn. They will remain arched over me, branches drooping down, but I will be with him so that only their own essential, beautiful solitude is left.

I sense that he is close, my true love. Does he wait for me also?

I can almost feel his breath on my neck as he leans in to kiss me. He is not far off. Be brave, I tell my soul. Keep strong. You will be together soon. The blackbird, bursting into song after the rain has promised as much.

I am the smoky atmosphere of Ronnie Scott's long after midnight. I am the dust-covered table in the Patisserie Valerie on Sunday afternoon. I am the thin, tapered fingers of the piano player in the restaurant next door. I was in love with a man once but he never knew.

I can't settle. I am restless and ambitious. I ache for something deep in my soul that I cannot describe. I return to writing and books. To my first loves. Warming my winter-dulled spirit with the fires of my imagination, I conjure pictures from the flames. Of impossibly beautiful things.

Jim, of course, is as yet unaware of my longing for him. He is getting to grips with his new life, working on a building site, conquering his fear of heights as he rides up and down a high rise block of flats in a makeshift lift. It rattles and shakes with the effort of ascending, but like his new found determination, it won't let him down.

Later he finds respectability – an office job in the civil service. He wears his suit with pride; it's not an expensive one but it cost him nearly everything he has just the same. The temptation to turn back to his old path is gone. His occasional forays into gambling keep the worst of the deep primal need for oblivion at bay. He has his head above water at last and gazing out across the sea front, he can almost glimpse the horizon in the distance.

PART 4

CHAPTER 25

I am seeking the happiness of my childhood Narnia, a springtime woodland that fell into the hands of a white witch long ago. She cursed the Kingdom with her icy spell, making it forever winter. A fox, struck down on the road, now lies resplendent before me in the gutter, his russet pelt covered in snow, no more to trot beneath a moonlit night.

But I have heard the whisper he is coming. I have heard that Aslan is on the move...

A poster advertising an amateur production of The Lion, The Witch and The Wardrobe greets my eyes at the Arts Centre. Busy in rehearsal, a gaggle of young children swarm past me, pursued by a haughty White Witch in full costume. Wolves lurk close by, no doubt, ears pricked, listening intently, for she has her spies everywhere. I climb the stairs to where the writers meet. I am Jim's future wife and any second now, our paths will collide.

Jim has no idea what is about to happen. Me? I sense that something is afoot and hug myself in anticipation, shivering, although admittedly it is a freezing cold night. All the people who have already assembled are at least twenty years my senior. I catch sight of a white-haired woman in an expansive shawl, her eyes like blue marbled glass as she reads Isherwood. I wonder if Isherwood ever doubted his ability to write?

Jim knocks on the door. I look up. Mine is the first face he sees. He is extraordinarily beautiful, this stranger, who is, nevertheless, uncannily familiar to me. Astonishingly thick eyelashes frame the windows of his soul. I have never, in all my life, seen such an exceptional man. His dark hair and olive skin remind me of Italian summers, but when he speaks, he has a strong Glaswegian accent and my bones melt at the lilt of his voice.

"Hi! You're new, aren't you?"

When he leans forward to shake my hand, I feel the electricity sparking between us.

"I'm Kerry," I smile.

"Kerry?" He sounds pleased. "I'm Jim. This is Charles, and Kier and Bonita and..."

Suddenly I am warm and at home, intensely grateful to him for breaking the ice. He winks and settles down in his seat, still smiling.

Mesmerised, I watch him from a distance, as he effortlessly conducts the meeting. I long to impress him with my words, reading out the first page of my intended novel. I have no idea of the ending yet, but looking at him, my confidence is restored. He listens intently, his eyes alighting on me like butterflies, lovely to behold.

"You are coming next week, aren't you?" He demands afterwards, helping me on with my coat. I nod vigorously, desperate not to reveal that I am in love with him already.

Outside, in the clean crisp air, I exhale deeply, alive with joy. I have been looking for him my whole life and now I have found him. Deep certainty resides in my soul as I sail home under a bowery of golden street lamps which illuminate the windows of the terraced houses opposite. When we are walking down the street, he and I, hand in hand, angels will dance alongside us in the dark.

The snow is falling steadily still, yet a curious shift is taking place. Jim senses it too when he puts his key in the front door and steps inside. His heart is slowly melting.

We swim past each other in the night, in our dreams. Our longing for each other is immortal and as fathomless as time. Somewhere, before, we have met, but in this temporal world, we must begin anew.

Love is a negotiation both thrilling and terrifying, conducted one step at a time. Glancing and retreating. Deeper magic is at work. He is, undoubtedly, on the move…

The daffodils have triumphed over winter. As they aim their determined trumpeted heads towards the light, they form an impromptu jazz band in the park. The sun emerges briefly like a sleepy dreamer, casting its warmth across the earth, before retiring again beneath a duvet of clouds.

Soon Jim will be mine and I will be his, as surely as the waves return to shore.

I cannot eat. I cannot sleep. I cannot stop smiling at the world and all that's in it. Comfort me with apples, for I am sick with love! Friends pause to take my temperature, laughing, certain that my serene mood is a sign that I am coming down with something.

Jim turns up in the most unexpected of places. I collide with him one lunchtime. As he waves urgently to me, he nearly knocks over the blonde girl who is with him. I see her flashing smile and blue eyes and experience the quiet devastation of believing he must, after all, be married.

Inexplicably, he then appears the following day in the pub next door. He gives me a wink, pinches a chip from my plate and vanishes without a word out of the door. He is trouble, I grin. I like that.

Finally, I spot him calling to me from the ground floor window of the office block I work in. For three years, it transpires, we have both worked here! Why did our paths never collide until now?

"I can't believe this!" I announce, dumbfounded as we stand together in the corridor.

"I know! Mental, isn't it?" He grins.

Friday night he catches up with me after work.

"I wondered if you fancied coming out for a drink with me one night?" He asks, his voice gruff, his eyes dark and expecting disappointment. He braces himself for the knock back he is expecting.

"I'd love to!" I am beaming.

"Oh, well, never mind. I just thought I'd ask anyway," he replies, nodding resignedly. "Have a good weekend, won't you?"

Waving, he is gone.

I stand defeated, watching the cars swirling around the roundabout before finally crossing to the other side of the road.

What on earth did I do wrong? How did I misread the clues? I torture myself, lying on the settee at my friend Bob's house, agonised with love.

"I need a drink, Bob."

Bob grins, hands on hips, floury from the kitchen where he is baking a pie.

"Come on then, sweetheart, tell me his name! You know you can always talk to your Uncle Bob."

So I do. I tell him everything. Uncle Bob has seen it all before.

Jim is annoyed with himself. Of course I wouldn't be interested in him, would I? He's too old for me, for a start, isn't he? Giving him the brush off, like that? He should have seen it coming. What an idiot, not reading the signs. Now he feels foolish. He sticks a record on and pours himself a brandy, trying to drown out the objections of his heart.

Everywhere I go, Jim's face sails before me. Work slides past my desk and hopefully past my boss, unnoticed. Angels, in the guise of colleagues, step in on my behalf, for I am lost in heavenly realms. I am eight pounds lighter than when we met two weeks ago. I fit my clothes perfectly. My lips are rosebuds, yearning for his kiss.

What is it with this man? He infuriates me and fascinates me in equal measure. Unless I am hopelessly misreading the situation, he does really like me. He watches me whenever I read in the group, but I glower at him in return. My face is a fire of furious blushing, but I will deny it has anything to do with him. I pretend I have no time for his nonsense.

It works remarkably well. He may even think I hate him but it doesn't prevent him from walking me to my bus stop every Wednesday, though. My bus is pulling up. It's now or never.

"Are you up to anything on Friday? Only I wondered if you fancied going for that drink you mentioned the other day?"

God, I can hardly breathe. I can scarcely believe this is me, speaking.

"YES! Yes. Definitely. I'll take you out for a meal. Or I can cook for you at my place if you prefer?"

The bus driver leans over his wheel, listening to our discussion.

"OK, yours it is!" I grin. "Then I'll get to see where you live too!"

"I'll meet you downstairs at work. Friday, 4 o'clock!" He calls.

I nod, casually, waving out the window to him.

*

The script Jim had been practising for some time is rendered obsolete. The careful prescription for a measured life of crushed hopes and deflated expectations has just been torn up and tossed into the nearest bin. He treasures these new feelings of his. They defy logic, but all the same, he has a spring in his step as he walks home tonight.

Me? I play it cool until the bus has safely turned the corner. Only then do I shriek with delight. I am in love and I do not care who knows it!

CHAPTER 26

Our first date is on Valentine's Day. Even the saints have conspired in our favour.

Jim takes my gloved hand tenderly in his and we cross the road together. It is bitterly cold. The puddles form silvery mirrors on the pavement, reflecting the street lights that illuminate the dark.

Up the front steps of the old Victorian red brick building in Florence Road. He ushers me in first and I pull my gloves off one by one.

"Mind the carpet on the stairs, it's a bit loose," he warns, anxious I do not trip.

Nervously he unlocks the door to his bedsit and I step inside.

"Here you are! Come and sit in the comfy chair and let me take your coat."

I sink down gratefully into the armchair.

"Do you want a coffee? Or brandy? How about both?"

I smile. "That would be great, thank you."

Nescafe and brandy. One in a mug, one in a brandy glass. I set them on the little wooden table to my right.

"Do you like music? I'll put a record on."

I do. I startle him with the breadth of my appreciation.

"How do you know all these bands?" He demands, suspiciously. "You were about three when this one came out?"

I smile knowingly. I have loved music for as long as I have lived.

We settle for Lou Reid. Obligingly, Mr. Reid clears his throat and cracks on with his New York album. Romeo has his Juliet right there.

The vinyl record spins around as the pasta hits the saucepan. Lou Reid's biting sarcasm and wit accompany Jim's diligent cooking on the tiny stove directly behind me.

Cast aside your preconceptions but make no mistake that this is a room where middle aged men go to live when their dreams have deserted them. A place where they are discovered dead in bed by the landlord one Monday morning. The typewriter, placed defiantly on the table beside Jim's own bed, spouting letters and poems, aches to tell a different story.

Writing is Jim's last hostage to fortune. The unapologetic outpouring that belies his humble surroundings.

The bed, covered in regulation sheets and blankets, is prison issue in all but name, devoid of home comforts, save for the crocheted blanket Margaret supplied him with years before. Piles of magazines and newspapers are stored on the floor. A small television in the corner keeps him connected to the outside world. If you listen hard, you can make out the pounding beat of night clubs and the wail of police sirens along the sea front outside. Life is out there, somewhere.

Jim's books and poetry serve to protect him. They line the shelves and walls of his fortification. The drawbridge is raised to deter outsiders and only the privileged few make it into his inner sanctum. The army of dissenting voices in his head are summarily drummed out with music. Zappa, Bowie, Talking Heads, Love, Captain Beefheart.

Bring it on! Let life throw whatever it dare in Jim's direction. He is ready to meet it head on. He has seen and dealt with worse.

There is no central heating. Even in the depths of winter, he relies entirely on the three bar electric fire. He cannot afford to keep it on as often as he would like. Poverty is a desperate state of affairs, especially the effort it costs to conceal it. You are not allowed to be this poor if you intend to be respectable too.

His clothes, he washes carefully by hand, in the sink,

hanging them over a clothes horse to dry by the inadequate electric fire. The tiny sink stands above a cupboard in the corner, next to the stove. The edges of the torn wallpaper are yellowing, indicating the futility of it all. If I peel them back far enough, will they reveal how this happened to Jim?

"I thought you wouldn't turn up tonight," he announces, matter of fact, raising his brandy glass to mine.

"Why?"

"Because I thought you'd come to your senses and think, What do I want to be going out with a miserable old bastard like him for?"

"Rubbish! I've been really excited all week – you miserable bastard!"

He is secretly pleased, but says nothing.

"You are daft," I continue, softly.

"Who are you calling daft?" His eyes flash mischievously and he grins. "Anyway, I'm very glad you came. Do you like pasta?"

I nod.

"Good job too, cos that's what we're having for tea."

He ladles two large portions onto our plates. We sit and watch a comedy, perched one in a chair and one on the bed, our dinners balanced on our laps. We are warm and hopelessly in love and it simply doesn't get any better than this.

Jim is a collector of Nescafe coffee labels and Marlboro cigarette packet liners. He has a wealth of finery to show for his efforts.

"Look," he beams, showing me a T-shirt with a cowboy riding across Marlboro country on it. Lassoed by the comfort of free gifts, he is a boy again, pleased with his presents. Somebody out there loves him, even if it is only a corporation willing to reward his brand loyalty.

"I got a leather wallet with it too." He pauses, suddenly realising the folly of it all and is briefly crestfallen.

"Stupid really, isn't it?"

He knows, you see, underneath, what this is really all about.

All the collecting in the world will not bring him what he is really searching for.

Jim's records are meticulously arranged in strict alphabetic order. Ironic, such attention to detail, given the chaotic state of the rest of his room. Papers lie abandoned on the floor. Poems cling for dear life to the edges of the table, in danger of falling forgotten into the wastepaper bin below. A collection of short stories accompany his forays into the world, folded neatly in his pockets, talismans that offer protection, guarding his heart. He goes out onto the landing to have a cigarette and I join him. My eyes water in a haze of drifting smoke and he is sorry, but I don't mind. I just want to be with him.

Back in the room, I sit on the floor, Jim in the chair, my back leaning against his knees. He puts Zappa on, testing my reaction. If I pass, I get to graduate to Captain Beefheart. Some reward, I grin sarcastically and he pulls a face. He strokes the top of my head tenderly and plants a kiss on it, making certain I am real and not a dream, about to fade away.

He is sad beneath that smile of his. Bewitching too. He doesn't need anyone. He can survive anything. He has proved it to himself time and time again, but what if he wants to do more than just survive?

I hesitate for a second as he draws me towards him for a kiss, as if I am witness to something from which I can never turn back. Then, nestling in his arms, I am lost to him. He is tall and his body is sturdy and solid, but he is possessed of a giant's gentleness. His eyes gaze out with inexpressible tenderness towards me.

Afterwards, in the pub, I sit nursing a vodka and lime. He has his hand outstretched across the table, covering mine.

"Got big old hands, haven't I?" He eyes them, ruefully.

They are huge; ruddy, cheery workman's hands, used to an outdoor life.

"Frank Zappa did a song once about big, old hands. I sometimes wonder if he wrote it about me!" He grins.

He wants to play the fruit machine. He is restless and doesn't quite know where to put himself but he knows it isn't right, disappearing on a first date, so he stays put.

"Go on – it's fine!" I assure him, grinning.

"Will you stand beside me? Bring me good luck?"

I slip my arms through his coat sleeves. He kisses me on the cheek.

Jim is taking the biggest gamble of his life did I but realise it. When he feeds the first coin into the machine, the stakes seem reasonable enough. He can endure the loss if need be. But life has a habit of demanding more of him. To Jim, it is everything, this business of winning and losing. The real gamble he's taking is the one on his heart.

We return to our table and he shakes his head.

"I shouldn't play them, really. I don't know why I do." He lights a cigarette and draws on it.

I don't know why he does either. Not yet.

Outside, the stars are scattered like tiddlywinks across the night sky. The moon has retired to bed like a sulky child, refusing to clear up first, so there they must remain until morning.

He stops me for a moment. "Which is your favourite star?"

"Easy," I reply. "The North Star. First out and brightest. Yours?"

"Me? I prefer the third one from the left!" He grins.

*

Love has blinded us both to reality. I believe in fairy tales because I never fail to see my Prince. I would recognise him whatever disguise the world saw fit to throw over him. However ill-fitting that glass slipper may yet prove to be, I will never stop insisting I can walk just fine in it.

We dance in slow procession down the road, intertwined in our song of love. Me in my imaginary glass slippers, desperately staring at the clock through the window of the pub as we pass, fervently hoping that the Coach and Horses pub will not turn into a pumpkin come closing time.

He scribbles his telephone number on a piece of cardboard torn from a cereal packet. It's one of his competition tokens that he had been saving, but tonight he has his eyes on a different prize.

"Will you come back and see me on Sunday?" He pleads, his eyes lit with longing. I nod furiously. I wave and wave from the bus window until he is out of sight. I have left him clutching my glass slipper. It will fit no one else now. Besides, what's the use of one shoe without the other matching one?

CHAPTER 27

I don't have any wild expectations. Being with him is enough. There is no hidden agenda. I simply love this man deeply. To me, utter bliss is sitting tucked between his legs, watching TV, with a mug of Nescafe warming my hands. Whoever thought heaven was unreachable from earth has clearly never been in love.

Practically speaking, it will not be easy for us to marry or raise a family. There is the age difference for a start. I am 23 to his 39. I've seldom yearned for domesticity, so I leave everyone else to worry about my prospects. All I can do is trust exactly where I am.

The steam from the kettle has blurred the mirror above the sink in his room with condensation. Dare I wipe the glass clear and see what is really underneath? I decide against it. I am not ready yet to confront the truth. I scribble my name on the surface with his, then wipe it clean impatiently with the back of my sleeve, embarrassed in case he sees it. I stare back at my own face. I am no scryer. Even if I could foresee the future, I would be powerless to prevail against it. Let time destroy us, if it must. We are trapped here, he and I. There is no other moment than now and when this is gone, there will be no other time but this.

One of the mugs has a chip in it, but he is always careful to give me the good one. He is up to his neck in debt and admits as much to me. He signed as guarantor on a loan for a friend who proved to be anything but and jumped ship without settling with the bank. Jim sets about paying it back, quietly accepting the injustice of it all.

Saturday afternoons pass in a blur. We lie, arms wrapped around each other, on the bed, him drifting off to sleep, me wide awake, just dreaming. Counting the breaths, the rise and fall of his chest, I synchronise them with my own.

In the mornings, he wraps me up in a big towel and pops his dressing gown around me before I risk setting off to the bathroom opposite. Trekking across the landing, I expect to run into Captain Scott and his team, pausing to retrieve food supplies and tend to their huskies.

"I'm just going out and may be some time!"

Jim is gallantly off to get the papers. When he returns, we will sit eating Boost Bars for breakfast. I will perch on his knee, squashing the Sunday supplements and he will pretend not to mind.

He smokes Marlboro Lights out on the landing. If this was Texas, he'd be surveying his ranch, but it is provincial England, so he confines his wanderings to his indoors instead.

"I think I'm going to write a poem!" He announces brightly. Pulling up his chair, he settles himself down at the typewriter. A hush descends as he bravely traverses the tightrope of his imagination, no net beneath him should he fall, trusting the words to keep him upright. They have never once let him down.

"Want to hear it?" He beams eagerly at last.

There is only ever one answer to give.

Two players absorbed in a game of love. Time starts now. First kiss, first date, shake the dice. Miss a go. Your turn. First night together. How does it feel the next morning, waking up together? Two steps forward. Our first row, take a step back.

Love doesn't follow any of the rules. It is wild, untameable and glorious.

I am so happy right now, I think I might explode. I long to forge ahead with our story, to know in advance how it will all unfold. But for now, I must content myself with lying sandwiched between the wall and Jim's back, in bed, hoping he doesn't turn over unannounced, for if he does, I will surely suffocate.

Ridiculous, really, both of us squeezing into a single bed. By throwing my arms around his stripy T-shirted body, pillion style, I can hang on to this giant bumble bee of a man who is prone to buzzing with irritation if I snore. Suspicious of the flower in his bed who might, after all, turn out to be poisonous, he lies in my arms, dreams uneasily, stirs readily. Now and then he announces his next move ahead of schedule to enable me to adapt accordingly. We are conjoined twins, blissfully synchronised in love.

In the night, when he can't sleep, he wakes me up to natter in the dark.

"I knew a man in Glasgow once who…" he begins.

Or

"Did I ever tell you about the time that…?"

He would prefer to be alone, really. He would feel less self-conscious about pacing up and down, making tea in the small hours of the night or having a quick swig of brandy.

I wonder how anyone copes sleeping alongside a man who wakes fitfully every half hour on the dot? Why can he not settle, I wonder, exasperated? His legs are restless, pedalling the pavements of his dreamscape, as if he was astride a bicycle. Often I give up early on and park myself in the big armchair, his ancient white dressing gown, its pockets full of cigarettes and stories, warding off the chill.

The carpet is frayed. It never occurs to me that even the ancient furniture does not belong to him. There is so little to which he can attach any meaning or sense of personal history. No wonder his typewriter is so revered. It is the pivot on which his life continues to turn. Am I any closer to understanding him?

"You're getting warmer," he might whisper, lost in sleep. Privately, I doubt it. Those eyes harbour dark secrets. Now and then I see them mist over with the effort of containment.

You can hear it in songs, if you listen carefully enough. Or in the lull between the waves on a winter's beach. It is carried on the tide. The restless longings of the human heart. Seagulls hover overhead, the souls of ancient mariners carried in their cries. Geese in the distance, silent but for the tread of their wings, migrate here in search of what they cannot find at home. We are travellers here, all of us. We have come in search of love and meaning and we will not go to our rest until we carry both in our hearts, certain that they exist.

I see in Jim a destination I have sought my whole life. Being with him is utterly magical. I am afraid of reaching in too close and destroying our gossamer beauty. My heart is stripped bare, laid out before him. I lie with my head on his chest, listening to his heartbeat, hoping to hear within its furious depths the longing I too possess.

We have washed up on an unsuspected shore of blankets and pillows, startled to discover we are such kindred spirits.

Outside, the heart of winter is melting into spring, pooling its tears into puddles. We skip the worst of the rain and hide in the pub. At night, we walk along the seashore, listening to the waves crashing wildly in the dark. In daylight, I hop down on to the pebbles, searching out pieces of translucent glass, washed smooth by the sea. Or the tiny shells, coiled and pearlescent, perfectly diminutive. He leans in to me, throwing an arm around me to keep the gales at bay. I dip my hands into his pockets, filling them with my wordless treasures. We kiss. Our love is unspeakably deep, washed up like the ocean on shores all over the world. We are all the lovers who preceded us and all the lovers who will come after us.

I start to nest. The restless nature that once consumed me has found a focus in him. I buy him proper food and cook him casseroles. He needs to eat properly, I chide, concerned by his diet. He eats hungrily, like a grateful child. Hot stews, leeks, carrots, onions. They take hours to prepare on such a tiny stove. We use brown bread to soak up the juices and the gravy. He looks better for it, less chilled. He wipes his lips and pulls my ear affectionately for a laugh. I smooth his face and see in my cool, gentle touch, an unconscious fragment of my mother's love.

CHAPTER 28

Jim holds a torch for an old flame.

He has a photograph of her. An ethereal ghost of a girl, with auburn hair, dressed in a leather jacket and jeans, gazing directly at him.

I think she must have loved him once. I resent her intrusion into our relationship. I can tell she meant something to him at one time. Perhaps she still does?

"You worry about things too much," he assures me.

Claire. I only know her name. I scrutinise his face, as if, at any moment, he will cave in and admit the truth.

"I did love her once."

"And now?"

He shakes his head, indicating too much time has passed. I do not believe him. I sense there is more than he will tell me.

My life is an open book. Start anywhere, read me cover to cover and it's all there.

Who are you, Jim? Harder to read, less accessible, and not for the faint hearted. You present me with a challenge.

I set about my detective work diligently. My gloved hands inspect the books on your shelf while you sleep. Joe Orton, Flann O'Brien, J. P. Donleavy. Decoys among them, no doubt. Other people's paperbacks that you borrowed and neglected to return. Surely they must wonder why, three years on, you are still only halfway through Beautiful Losers?

Poetry abounds. Who is the woman who wrote the inscription

on this nature book? I burn with not knowing, wishing I had never looked. You reawaken and I leap into the armchair.

"Sorry about that, I must have drifted off," you beam, entirely without suspicion.

I am not finished with you yet, Jim McPhail. Later, I plan to read the backs of all your postcards, dotted about the walls. I am insatiable in my curiosity, determined to piece you together.

"Ready then?" You ask and we are off to read our words at our beloved Arts Centre.

Bitingly cold out, again, isn't it? Just as we thought the weather was easing, too. Careful you don't slip on that ice. It wouldn't take much. We cling to each other, skating uneasily across the surface of our new love. It's tentative, the faith we have in each other, isn't it? It appears to be solid, but it's surprisingly fragile underneath.

At the writing group, you produce a story with a magician's flourish.

"This is about a man I once knew in Glasgow."

Davie appears from nowhere and springs to life on the page, tormenting everyone anew. Who is he, to you, I wonder? This despicable yet pitiable figure you describe so clearly. The story is alight. All eyes watch you as you read. Are you really unaware of the impact your words have as they leap with the intensity of flames from the page? A terrible truth emerges from the fire. A warning about the true cost of redemption. As you reach the end, I lean forward, instinctively, anxious to protect you. You drop the paper to the table just in time. The memories that flare up, threatening to engulf you, are extinguished by the reality of the present moment.

"That man?" I begin, asking what is on everyone's lips. "You knew him well, didn't you?"

Jim's fiction does not fool me.

He nods, eyeing me warily.

"He was my stepfather."

"So it was your home that caught fire?"

He lights up a cigarette and exhales breezily. "Cheery bastard, aren't I?" He grins, apologetically. He has no need to. This was an act of exceptional bravery on his part, exposing himself to the truth.

I eye his huge hands, chapped and raw. The same hands that sought to rescue a dying man.

I am getting nearer to the truth at last.

He pulls back from me slightly and kisses me on the nose.

"Do they ever hurt, your hands?" I take them gently in my own.

"Nah! They just look terrible."

"Well, I think they are beautiful and I think you are incredibly brave."

Little by little it all comes pouring out. Over the years, Jim has done his best to stamp out the fire that has raged through his inner landscape but it frequently threatens to overwhelm him.

"I was addicted to heroin for fifteen years, that's why my hands are really like this," he says quietly, once we are safely back in his room.

They are chapped and swollen, his hands. The veins that wend their way haphazardly across the backs are like knots of fine blue thread. I am stunned into silence by this fresh revelation.

"They look awful," he sighs, looking downcast. "But it's my own fault. The veins collapsed where I used to inject in them."

"I thought you'd burnt them. In the fire," I begin, cautiously.

He shakes his head. "I've been clean for seven years now. I went to Alpha House in Droxford. That's why I came down from Glasgow in the first place.

"Well, I think you are amazing. Well done!" I am awed by his strength of character. "It must have been impossibly hard. Coming off drugs, I mean?"

Jim nods. "Terrible."

"Do you ever... I mean... have you ever been tempted, since...?"

Jim shakes his head fiercely. "I'll never touch it again. I hated what it did to me and more than that, I hate what it did to everyone I loved."

Out of the corner of my eye I catch sight of Claire's photograph.

"Did she... did she know? About the drugs?"

Jim nods. "She used them too."

I am relieved he has told me, but I know not to push him any further even though I sense there is more to come. Now is not the right time. It is enough that he has started to confide in me.

Later, I wonder if he has told me the whole truth or whether I have been incredibly naïve. When he disappears to the bathroom, or goes for a cigarette out on the landing, is he secretly shooting up? I cannot ask anyone else. I do not know anyone who has ever used heroin.

I love him, that's all I know.

"Jim used to take heroin, years ago, but that's all stopped now," The words trip gaily off my tongue as I confide in my mother over coffee the next day, gauging her reaction. She has not met Jim yet.

"I wouldn't mention that bit to your father just yet," she advises, matter of factly.

He can't win, Jim, can he? He spent years getting clean and now he only wants to tell the truth about his situation, but it seems that other people can't cope with him coming clean.

CHAPTER 29

Jim is in full confessional mode. I might as well be a priest, sat the other side of a metal grille, listening to him. It's all coming out now.

"I was in prison once," he announces, coughing nervously and swallowing hard.

"Oh." I am watching Coronation Street and barely bat an eyelid while he continues massaging my neck and shoulders.

He leans forward, wondering if I have heard him properly.

"Do you want to know why?"

"Mmmmn. Of course." Just as soon as Sally Webster decides what she is going to do about Kevin, I will be all ears.

"Did you say prison?" I exclaim, turning around.

"I was done for possession. I got three weeks in Barlinnie on remand."

Barlinnie? It sounds like a Russian ballet company to me, but I doubt the similarities.

"In Glasgow?"

He nods, shuddering at the recollection, with a mixture of fear and embarrassment.

"What was it like? Was it awful?"

"Terrible. I was in solitary for a week, in an observation cell. I thought I was going mad. I was so scared. I cried myself to sleep every night while I was coming off heroin. Then they put me in the hospital wing. One of the old timers, Tommy Doone, helped me through it. He was great. I'll always be grateful to him.

Jim's fortitude inspires me. I think about spam sandwiches and tea in plastic cups and shudder.

He finds it baffling that I am still here. He wonders what it will take to make me walk.

Long after I am gone, Jim lies awake, alone in his single bed. His eyes take in the shadowed typewriter to his left, the hump back outline of the armchair, drooping like an old man, rudely illuminated by the street lamp outside. He thinks he hears a rustling in the garden down below. It is 3 a.m. No doubt the fox is rooting around in the dustbins.

He gets up and wanders over to the window, pulling the curtain back sufficiently to glimpse outside. There he is! He gazes up at Jim, with black shining eyes, briefly transfixed, then scuttles off along the wall, a chicken bone clamped between his jaws, leaving a trail of disturbed cartons and junk in his wake. Jim had been dreaming, hadn't he? About being back in Glasgow. He rubs his chin thoughtfully and decides to make himself a cup of tea. Sticking the kettle on, it comes back to him. Claire was in it. She had come to tell him she was leaving.

He shivers and pulls his dressing gown tightly around him. It isn't enough, so he throws his jumper around his shoulders too. He sits there in the chair, like a human clothes horse, squashing the papers because he can't be bothered to get up again. How does he live? How does he manage to keep a foot in both camps? The past constantly demands his attention. Yet he reaches forward, expectantly, to the future, tormented by his inability to be free and at peace in the present.

He gazes at the shot of me he took earlier. My face smiles back at him from the picture. He is weighing up how much else to tell me. It has been keeping him awake for days, wondering how I will react.

In the dream Claire told him there was somebody else. She looked sad. She had come to tell him she was leaving him, years after she had already moved away.

"Who is it?" He had asked her, in the dream, scarcely able to believe she was going.

"You know who she is." She whispered to him, kissing him on the cheek. "You told me about her yourself, remember?"

Jim feels the tight grip of sorrow, thinking of her. "Don't go," he whispers to himself in the dark.

He wants to explain to her how dreadfully sorry he is for everything. How can he? It is years since they last saw one another. He wrote to her, care of her mother, afterwards. He wanted her to know that he loved her, that he was desperately sorry for it all. Her mother wrote back immediately, a nicely worded letter that left him no clue as to whether Claire had read his letter or not. She is doing well. She has met a nice man in England. Is she still in England? He wonders, folding the letter up in his lap. Does she hate him? Does she blame him?

He hates himself, right enough. He drains the last drop of his tea. Guilt has riddled his bones and paralysed him with worthlessness.

It is too early to stay up and see in the dawn but he is too restless to return to sleep. He turns on the TV to distract him from the thoughts racing around his head. A cop car pursues a getaway driver down a one way street in New York.

Perhaps it would be easier to call the whole thing off? He can return to his uncomplicated life and pretend none of this ever happened. Better than risking everything. He looks at my picture again; I'm still smiling back at him. He senses briefly that he cannot give up. Why did he risk it? Why did he let himself be fooled into thinking he could fall in love again? He doesn't deserve love.

I sleep on. A mile up the road, I am blissfully unaware of his torment. My own dreams are filled with jam jars and butterflies and other nonsense, but that is my own fault for eating cheese on toast too late at night.

*

Curiosity gnaws at me, in spite of what Jim has already told me.

I rummage in his wardrobe, incidentally breathing in the scent of him on his coat and jumpers but searching for more clues while he is safely out of the room. A childish notion forces me to test the back of the wardrobe, pushing against it; just to make sure it does not open into a snow filled land of Narnia.

Jim is coming up the stairs. I exit sharply. We settle in front of the electric fire. He is reading, or pretending to. We bask in silence. I am curled up, my head resting in his lap, while he strokes my hair, trying not to set it on fire with his cigarette end.

Suddenly he begins to cry gently. When I look up, his shoulders are shaking and tears are rolling down his cheeks.

"Whatever is it?" I entreat, taking his hands. I hold my head to his chest and he smoothes my hair unsteadily.

"Is it Claire? Are you still in love with her?" I ask gently.

He clutches her photograph to him and my heart sinks. He is going to leave me for her, I am certain of it. He continues to sob, quietly ashamed of the tears streaking down his face, burying his hand in his pocket in search of a tissue.

"Here," I hand him my own.

He will never love me the way he loves her, I suppose. Even knowing that, I cannot bear seeing him so upset.

"You asked me why we split up and I never told you," he says.

"I had no business asking," I reply, lightly.

"The truth is, it was awful. A gang broke into the flat we lived in. They were looking for two men who used to live there who had drugs they were after. They broke the door down. Arthur was with us. They beat us both to a pulp, Arthur and me, and pushed us into a room. By the time I broke free of them and went to find Claire, they'd…" he cannot get the words out. He is choking on his tears. "They'd…"

"It's OK," I plead. "Just stop. You don't have to say any more, if you don't want to."

"They held her down and one of them… he… raped her,"

The silence rings in our ears. His devastation is total. I cradle his head in my hands and hold him to me. The girl in the photograph with the beautiful auburn hair and green eyes stares wordlessly back at us both.

"I couldn't save her. I was too weak." He is shaking with rage and sorrow.

I draw my breath in tightly. The horror of the moment is written in his eyes, as if it is unravelling right now in front of him.

"It wasn't your fault..."

"I couldn't save her. I was her partner and I couldn't stop them." He stares wildly at me and he sobs as if his heart will break.

I hold him for a long time. Sometimes he hears her screaming still. He doesn't tell me this. I find out, long after.

I blow out the candles on the mantelpiece one by one and the room around us descends into darkness. It will never again swallow him up. I will keep guard over him always and keep him safe. Fire will not come near him. It will not torment him again, while I am here.

PART 5

CHAPTER 30

The doorbell rings and I rush to greet you, busily adjusting my dress, toppling over in my high heels. I so want to impress you. Will you take a chance, Jim, on it all working out perfectly between us?

We can't get beyond the garden wall without pausing for a kiss. Passers-by whistle at us but we just grin. Let the fireworks commence. June is bursting into life as we wend our way down to the sea front where the bands are setting up to play. A summer music festival. Tonight everything sparkles like champagne and we are effervescent with love. When we return, the stars are dancing above the rooftops. Will you stay the night? No words. None needed. It's OK. I understand you perfectly. I cradle your head in my hands. We are king and queen of this palatial studio flat I rent, our kingdom spreads out royally before us. A stone's throw from the kettle, even when we are in bed. You could almost throw the bread into the toaster from here.

The sofa sails by on its regal ocean of blue rug, its crew of cushions standing to attention as it passes. Or am I drunk with wine and the flush of love? Did the room move for you too? I kick my heels shy of the bed. All our clothes lie on the floor together, as if, following an emergency drill, we were forced to jump clear of them at a moment's notice. I half expect your trousers to bow respectfully and invite my dress to dance.

I can't take it seriously, this love business. I am beaming from ear to ear, my hair awry, my face lit up with roses. You? You look so happy, reclining on the bed, your dark exotic eyes dancing across my body.

I steal a swig of brandy from your glass, revelling in your indignation. Pinch me, Jim, to make sure I am not dreaming. Will you still be here come morning, or will I turn to pat the space beside me to find you gone?

I blurt it out in the end, unrehearsed.

"I love you too," you reply, in a heartbeat.

"You do?" It feels so good to hear it.

"Of course I do." Intimacy has drawn us closer together than a pair of curtains. See? There was nothing to be scared of after all.

I could lie here all day, watching you. Wrapped up in your arms, safe as a banker's salary increase. Not you, though. You are restless. Primal instincts drive you outdoors to forage for newspapers. When you return, I am lying where you left me, in our wild cave of a bed. Is it sunny out? I peer experimentally beneath the blinds. Hooray!

We'll make a day of it. Shops first, then lunch out, a walk beside the sea afterwards. What a performance they all made of it, the abandoned shoes and tights, last night. It wasn't half as nerve wracking as the dress rehearsal, was it?

We are word perfect now. I can only imagine the dazzling reviews. Opening the papers I expect to read about us both, but the real news of the day has clearly been lost on the reporters.

Later we find a pound coin on the pavement and we take it as a sign.

"Heads we go left, tails we go right!" I pronounce, laughing.

"Heads."

We follow the coin, thus, all the way to the town centre where it brings us to the betting shop at last.

We grin expectantly at each other.

"Got to be done!" We agree.

We put it on a horse running at ten to one. Predictably it romps home first. We walk out afterwards, a tenner up.

Lady Luck, it seems, cannot help but smile on us.

Towards midnight we return from a party. Trees and ornamental hedges rise up in the darkness, lit only by a pale sliver of moon. The edge of a teaspoon glints in our night time mugs as we drink, side by side, on the settee at mine.

How did we live before we met each other? Were all the days before us grey and nondescript like late November? From now one there will only be summer. Our world is thrust into colour. I am reminded of the Wizard of Oz, when Dorothy's beloved hometown is swept up in a cyclone and she emerges into the glorious technicolor land of Oz. I have been asleep among the poppies and cannot be roused. Jim daren't shake me awake for fear of disturbing such a beautiful dream. My companion in sleep is right beside me. I reach across to touch the tip of his nose. Just to make sure he is real. Just to be certain I am not imagining such happiness. Never has the world been more alive to possibility than it is now.

I wake to find him gone from the bed. Blinking, I see him silhouetted, standing by the window, gazing out at the moon.

Come back to bed, I entreat him, silently. Lean into me. I won't ever let you fall. He does not realise that I too am awake. He does not know that I am looking out for him, now and always.

CHAPTER 31

No matter how the sun may shine, how bright may be the skies,
The sweetest picture I can see, is the love light in your eyes
If all the world were mine to give, I give it yes and more
To be in Bonnie Scotland with the girl that I adore

A letter to Jim's mother, Margaret, written to her during wartime by her beloved Hugh, then stationed in Germany, brings memories flooding back. Lost in thought, she folds it carefully and replaces it in the bureau.

The girl to whom Hugh was writing is in her seventies now. A wee, undemonstrative woman with arthritic hands and an air of resigned bafflement at the cards life has dealt her. Yet dignity intact, she sticks the kettle on, glancing at the clock on the wall.

We are on our way to Glasgow, Jim and I, to see her. Travelling with friends, we sit in the back of their car, a timid Alsatian dog squashed like a teddy bear between us.

"Don't worry if my Mum doesn't talk to you," Jim confides in me. "It's nothing to do with you, honestly, it's just that she can be a bit awkward sometimes."

I am not worried. Mothers the world over approve of me. I should be stamped with a quality kite-mark. Nothing about my demeanour suggests I ever get drunk, smoke dope or hang around with unsuitable company. Dignity intact, I comb my hair and check my lipstick in the driver's mirror.

"She might object to me being English," I grin, teasing him.

"No, no, it's not that," Jim is amused now. "She has a habit of sending people to Coventry for no good reason. When I took my last girlfriend to meet her, she didn't say a word to her the whole week we were there."

This is all sounding reassuringly familiar to me. My own family bear a striking resemblance to Jim's.

Glasgow is full of ghosts. Jamaica Street is haunted by a phantom boy, astride his late father's motorbike. A beaming child clambers up the steps of the long vanished Wilson's Zoo, still carrying a bucket of bread for the lion. A lost adolescent hangs out in Kelvingrove Park, beneath a tree. The shadowy, hopeless form of a heroin addict lies slumped in a flat in West Princes Street.

Some of the ghosts are an ever present living reality to Jim. They take on the appearance of his long lost friends and walk the Byres Road in broad daylight. He is filled with trepidation and longing at the prospect of seeing them again.

Glasgow is vast. Driving along the underpass, the orange lights beaming dully through the mist, we talk animatedly. Jim points out Barlinnie Prison and I think of the prisoners waiting out their time inside.

The lights along the Clyde bear witness to the former glory of the shipyards. Towering above us on the hills are the vast estates of Drumchapel and Easterhouse. The comedian Craig Ferguson made a crack about them once, in his stand-up routine.

"They built Easterhouse for 26p. They could have done Drumchapel for the same but they wanted a shop!"

Shops are indeed few and far between for the residents. Visiting vegetable vans still toil up the hill twice weekly. Unimaginably bleak, the flats rise up like broken teeth from the jaws of the government's urban regeneration programme. Far below them, kids sit in burnt out cars, going nowhere.

It is dark when we arrive at West Princes Street.

"Hello, Mum," Jim gives Margaret a quick hug. She looks embarrassed and pleased all at once.

"This is Kerry," he continues, one arm around my waist.

Margaret nods and says, 'Hello'. This is progress.

A nudging at my knees indicates that someone else is pleased to see us. A dear salt and pepper covered head with limpid eyes gazes up at me, adoringly, desperate to be acknowledged.

"Oh, hello there! You must be Trixie? Aren't you gorgeous!"

The wiry haired mongrel wags her elderly tail delightedly as I sink to give her a cuddle.

"Careful she doesn't dribble all over you," grins Jim.

"Oh, she wouldn't do that, would you, darling?" I exclaim, ignoring the wet patch rapidly developing on my knee.

We get ready for bed in the spare room. Twin beds, directly facing each other. Like children forced into a corner, we giggle in the dark. There is a certain protocol demanded by Margaret's age and sensibilities. We cannot be too noisy. We kiss and hug but it is not easy and I pull away from Jim.

"I'm really sorry about this," Jim whispers. "I should have got us somewhere to stay, but she would have been so hurt."

"It's fine," I reassure him. It really is. After all, we have all the time in the world together.

I wonder briefly how Margaret feels as she prepares for bed, first wandering into the kitchen to give Trixie her final feed, then retiring to her bedroom. Placing her hair in a net before the mirror and smoothing her curls down. Seeing perhaps, in her son's eyes, a recollection of the love that she had once known with Hugh when he was alive.

The next morning we wake and Jim gazes across at me.

"Hello, you!" He grins.

"Hello back!" I wink.

A loud noise ensues from his bed.

"Was that you?" He grins, in mock consternation.

"You know fine well it wasn't!" I object, indignantly. He enjoys his joke, like a naughty child, whipping the duvet off me and forcing me to get up and kiss him.

He makes me a cup of tea while I get washed and dressed. The kitchen is a war zone. Unwashed dishes have invaded the sink and several tatty tea towels are waving in surrender, battling to retreat to the borders by the towel rail. Jim puts tin foil across the grill pan to preserve us from the worst of the grease and sets potato scones onto it.

"You'll like these," he promises.

Margaret enters, patting her hair and sinks down into her armchair. She doesn't take breakfast.

"Do you like tea?" she enquires.

"I certainly do." I reply.

"Me too. I'm a regular tea Jenny." She smiles, approvingly.

Satisfied I can be trusted, she sits and updates me on what is happening in Emmerdale Farm, before following it up with a swift resume of Take The High Road.

Jim is delighted we have hit it off so well.

Outside a biting cold wind eats into our faces and hands. We make it to the supermarket. Everything here is cut price. Everything is economy. The Scottish Breakfast tray with its Lorne sausage, fruit pudding, sliced black pudding and tattie scone is a revelation to me. An invitation to cast aside all government health warnings and fry to your heart's content to keep warm instead. The rain here alone could freeze the marrow in your bones. So you turn to Vodka and fried mince and tatties and fish suppers and hang the consequences.

We stride along Byres Road with its cafes and bookshops.

"Beth used to work in that record shop," Jim nods. "Me and Arthur would always pop in and borrow the latest LPs and take them home to listen to."

We stop outside a vegetarian café. The last Jim heard, Arthur was helping out here. Tentatively, he peers in, half afraid of finding him, yet longing to.

"Go on!" I urge, nudging his coat sleeve.

"No, I don't think he's there now," he declares stoutly. But I know he is merely afraid. He wants dearly to know that his friend is well, but he is so scared he will be disappointed.

It is nearly evening and I feel melancholy as we walk the streets. The red sandstone houses look warm and inviting. I sense Jim's own nostalgia. He is remembering a crowd of friends from long ago, laid out on the floor of a flat, listening to music, laughing, thinking they have all the answers.

Trixie is dreaming when we return. Flopped loyally at Margaret's feet, her wiry head rises up, acknowledging our return. Then she waddles over, generously offering herself up to be fussed over and surreptitiously eyes the biscuits Margaret has set out on the coffee table.

The fireplace forms the heart of the home. Above it are displayed the little knick knacks and comforts that Margaret has collected over the years. A tiny lamb nestles on a bed of china grass, a souvenir fairy hails from Stirling.

Margaret has had the photographs out. She hands me one, suddenly, while I am busy unbuttoning my coat.

"That was my second husband, Davie." She pauses, thoughtfully. "Ugly sod, wasn't he?"

Jim is startled and looks at me askance.

Of Hugh, Jim's father, Margaret says nothing. His memory is sacred. The chronicle of how much she loves and misses him is written on her face.

Balanced on the mantelpiece, above the fire, is a Scotsman figurine. He raises a tankard high in the air. Around his base are the legendary words, Whae's like us? Gie few and they're all deid.

Trixie returns to Margaret's side and stuffs her head on to her knee, gazing wistfully at her.

"Are you all right, ma wee pet?" She smiles a little sadly, then dreamily returns her gaze to the television.

Saturday comes and the living room is playing to a capacity crowd. Jim's family is wedged on the sofa in the style of the Simpsons cartoon. Kay, Jim's younger sister, dark haired and olive skinned, mischievous and cheery, sits beside her daughter, Wendy, and son, Derek. Beth sits beside them. Jim perches on the arm. Only the occasional raised eyebrow hints at any tension. Margaret suspects nothing and produces a roast chicken from the oven. There are roast potatoes, tinned green beans and fresh carrots too. Jim enjoys his meal, readily assenting to seconds. He chats busily and steadily with his sisters.

Afterwards, Jim and I go to see the statue of Lobey Dosser on the corner of Woodside Road. He is perched on top of his faithful steed, Elfie. Jim holds my hand, wary of looking too soft on his home territory. He is ever cautious of bumping into faces from the past.

"Jim? Is that really you?" He is cornered in a doorway outside a bookshop by a wee ginger-whiskered man with friendly eyes.

"Hamish? I don't believe it! How are you doing?" Jim shakes his hand.

"Yeah, I'm good thanks. You?"

"Yes, I got clean, thank God. Went to Alpha House down south in the end. It's been seven years now. Are you still working in rehab yourself?"

Indeed Hamish is. He relates a tale about a young heroin addict he has been terribly worried about.

"Wee lad has been in and out of care and had a terrible struggle. He resorted to stealing to fund his habit and got himself banged up."

"What happened to him?"

"He lost his leg last year. Had to have it amputated after he'd injected so much. It filled up with poison. He's only seventeen."

Jim is visibly shocked. "Tell me he's quit using now?"

"God, no," Hamish shakes his head. "Prison only hardened the poor wee bastard up. He got bitter, thinking no one cared at all about him. He's worse than ever now. Says it makes shoplifting a breeze. He staggers into a shop on his crutches, snatches up whatever he fancies and sticks it under his jacket and Bob's Your Uncle. If anyone dares to shoot him so much as an accusing look, he yells at them, 'You're staring at me just cos I'm a fucking cripple!' Of course, nobody wants to be seen to be politically incorrect so they back right away and off he goes to shoot up again. He'll be dead soon, right enough."

This is pronounced matter of factly but evidently Hamish cares desperately about the outcome. Jim too. They are both horrified because they have been there.

Hamish's words ring in my ears as we wander down Sauchiehall Street that afternoon. Not far from here, right now, a troubled amputee is hobbling down the road hating the world and all that's in it. I wonder if he will live to see his twenty-first birthday. I'm certain he never planned on being a one legged heroin addict when he grew up.

CHAPTER 32

Once back in England, Glasgow pours out into Jim's poetry, as if he is possessing his past in the only way left open to him. He is filled with nostalgia for his home city. His friends come to life in his writing, warmth and wit their hallmark traits. He could no more hope to hold onto them in reality than he could return for good to his former home.

One by one the death toll rises. Greg is found hanging from a tree, the victim of drug induced paranoia and delusions.

Paul succumbs to a heart attack. When Jim reads the news in a letter from his sister, he is unable to comprehend the reality of what has happened.

Every death steals a little of the life left in Jim. He is bruised by grief, carrying his scars deep within him. The pressing weight of guilt at surviving them pushes in on him. Arthur's death has the worst and final impact. He is found dead after a drinking session with distant acquaintances; they could hardly be called friends. The terrible unspoken suspicion is that Arthur may have been murdered.

They are all gone now, Jim's former pals. Drugs having begun their murderous assignation, they have continued to destroy. Like cancer cells, eating their host while remaining immortal themselves.

*

That chapter of Jim's life is now closed forever. However much he wishes for it, there is no last opportunity to build bridges. There is no going back.

He honours them with his tears and fond memories, eulogising them in words. I watch this gentle giant of a man nearly crushed under the weight of his feelings. My own words prove inept and inadequate. What do I know of grief? Life has been good to me. I am entirely unacquainted with its pains. Jim never holds it against me that I do not understand. In my ignorance, I am crassly dismissive of his losses. These are people he has not seen in years. I never think to set them against the backdrop of all that he has already endured in his life. Not once do I recognise that, for Jim, every loss acts as a lit touch paper, linking a chain of fire that burns all the way back to the starting point – the loss, as a child, of his beloved father. Of Davie's ordeal by fire. Of Claire's desperate screaming. It never goes away. There is only ever sorrow, only ever regret, only the awful, pressing burden of wishing it could all somehow have been different for them all.

He lays his ghosts to rest as best he can. At night they come to him in wordless dreams. Three friends and a flame-haired girl. A fire that ripped through his life and burned an indelible hole in his heart. A missing father, deeply longed for. It's a lot to carry around and pack in alongside our relationship. Sometimes there is barely room in the bed for the two of us at night. Do I wonder that he has trouble sleeping?

"You OK?" I whisper, clutching his shoulder.

"Course, just got something in my eye," he whispers, hoarsely. He won't entertain any notion of self pity. He's alive, isn't he? Unlike the others. He toughs it out, hardening his heart against love. He tests me out.

"I don't want a serious relationship."

"No, I know that," I reply.

Each morning, he plonks himself down on the side of the bed, putting his socks on, hardly caring that he is squashing my knees beneath the blanket as he does so.

"Ow! Get up!" I push him away.

"I think I need to spend a bit of time on my own," he growls.

"Fine, suit yourself." I retreat like a tortoise into my sulky shell. My heart is in shreds but I will not let him see. I get up and get dressed.

"Right, I'm off." I announce.

"Stay and read the papers for a bit." He softens.

I shake my head.

He nods. "You'll be OK?"

It is his way of saying sorry, of saying, "I don't quite know what's going on, bear with me."

"You just have a good rest." I smile tightly, heading out of the door.

"Call me later. Or I'll ring you. I'm sorry." He wants to reel back his lifeline now. He is sorry he had risked letting it out so far.

"Sure," I peck him on the cheek. I gaze wistfully at him for a moment. Not for the first time, it strikes me he is not looking very well.

Doubt has crept into our relationship. I question whether his heart is truly in it. He sees me as flighty and unreliable. I am like a moth, dancing towards a lamp and mistaking it for the moon. Soon I will singe my wings and it will be too late.

I throw my cards down on the table.

"If you want to go out with someone else, just let me know and I'll be off."

"I don't," he objects, scanning my face.

We skirt around each other, wary as rival tribesmen, each convinced the other is up to something. He sighs, as frustrated as I am with this stalemate. Our love is a tinderbox. We carry it carefully between us, edging around each other, aware that the slightest provocation could ignite the flames. When did the fault lines first appear? Was it Glasgow that came between us, reminding Jim of his past? Our once easy love has been shattered, exposing its fragility.

We bow our heads to the prevailing wind and march towards the sea front, determined to present a united front to the world. Jim puts a pound coin into a fruit machine at the arcade. He is playing them increasingly often. I stand by his side, watching.

"I think we need to talk," I begin.

Another coin goes in.

"What about?"

"You know what about!"

He grimaces, concentrating. Three cherries line up. A pound coin is duly dispersed by the machine and we are right back to where we started.

I don't have the strength for this. Why did they lie to you at rehab, Jim? You are no more free of addiction than you ever were. You relinquished heroin with one hand and grabbed alcohol and gambling with the other. The interminable inner wrestling of those age-old demons continues. Fearing love, you have raised a barrier to the world. Your fortifications are so solidly built that love cannot find a way to your heart. Unwilling to risk opening up to the dark recesses of your past, you batten down the hatches, convinced you will be safer that way.

*

Winter is coming on. I pull my coat tight around me as I walk home afterwards, crunching my dreams underfoot like fallen leaves. Snow is eddying around in flurries, brief and ineffectual. It will not settle and neither can I. At 3 a.m. I am still awake, sitting reading alone in my big double bed, drinking tea and listening to the chimes of the Guildhall clock. I wonder if Jim can hear them?

Chapter 33

I remember the boy in Aesop's Fables. He thrust his hand into a pitcher of filberts, eager to grasp as many as he could. Naturally he got his hand stuck. Unless he was willing to relinquish part of his haul, he could not safely remove it from the jug. But to do so meant losing some of his beloved filberts. So there he remained, hand trapped.

His dilemma is entirely Jim's own. Stranded between the familiarity of the past and the longing for a better future.

Jim has tried to grasp love, but he isn't sure what it looks like. The least threatening kind is that without any demand of commitment – the kind that a brief, meaningless flirtation with a married woman might offer. What is tougher and further out of reach is true love. Love that demands everything of him – truth, honesty and commitment. He likes the look of it but he isn't sure if he can afford it.

So he hedges his bets and tries for both, unwilling to relinquish either. Like the boy in the story, he finds himself in a rare old fix.

We become experts in restoration, papering over the cracks in our faltering relationship. We go to France for the day. It works at first, running away. We laugh and drink copious quantities of café au lait at pavement cafes, posing as poets. Jim smoking, me flicking my hair back from my face. A travesty of intimacy, the start of each new day offers only the chance to put more distance between us.

Except that neither of us can bear it – this constant waiting to see how things will turn out. Because I sense that I will never be enough for him, I start to push him away.

We walk along the quayside. Fishermen are examining their lobster pots and setting up an impromptu market stall. Crates on the sidewalk display pink and orange shellfish where the passing public can bend to inspect a fish or a lobster before buying. A crab escapes and scuttles sideways into the water, making a bid for freedom. I spot him out of the corner of my eye and cheer him on.

"I don't think things are working out between us," I venture, hands in pockets.

"Why do you say that?" He stops me, shocked.

"Well, I just don't think they are," I continue, making the observation with a casual air that belies the importance of my words.

I am desperate for him to convince me otherwise but he is numb. He looks upset and I am glad to see it matters to him.

I stare hard at the blue sky overhead until my eyes hurt from not blinking. In silence, we board the ferry home. Fear has crept between us like a shadow, ruining everything.

Days later, we've reached the point of no return. Two walking wounded, crossing no man's land, trying valiantly to support each other. I put the kettle on to boil, too afraid to acknowledge the dark feeling in the pit of my stomach.

In my absence, he has drawn up his battle plans to end all the torturous uncertainty once and for all. Charting the potential outcome with map pins and logic, Jim plots his course. I am walking towards him, with the cups in my hand, aware that he has the grenade poised, already in his hand. His last stock in trade. He is going to pull the pin and everything we've ever been to each other will be destroyed. I shut my eyes and a prayer races through my brain. Don't do it, please, I beg of you.

Too late. The bomb detonates. The room explodes. His words reverberate around the walls.

"I don't think we should see each other any more."

A deathly hush. My breath betrays my shock. I drop my cup. My hands cannot grasp it, the awful truth.

"You're not serious. Please." There is urgency in my voice. I cannot manage without him.

"I don't think I'm any good for you. I'm sorry."

He is not wrong. I am a wreck. I have been crying for weeks, in private, aware that I am slowly losing him.

Finally I get up from the debris, mustering what dignity I can. I put my coat on. I stagger out into the street, dark and silent. Did no one see what just happened in there?

He comes racing after me, but I am shell-shocked, numb with disbelief.

"Come on," he says, gently, "let me walk you home. It's the least I can do."

He kisses me on the forehead and I explode into tears.

"Oh, Kerry, I'm so sorry, believe me."

He puts his hand gently into mine but it hurts now. That sweet small gesture scorches, where once it brought only joy.

"Please, Jim, don't do this…" I am wrestling with my self respect, but it is already in shreds.

"I'm truly sorry," is all he can say.

Then I put my key in the lock, stepping over my dreams that lie broken in a million shards on the doorstep and go inside.

CHAPTER 34

Returning home at last, Jim sinks the last of his brandy from the bottle on the mantelpiece. He needs to force back the avalanche of his feelings. He has done the right thing, hasn't he? What else could he do? He can hardly explain his behaviour to himself, let alone expect anyone else to understand it.

Love, like a shadow, stealing across the room, had disguised its true breadth and height until the final moment of reckoning when he realised how terrified he was of his emotions. The postcards and missives pinned to the wall are snapshots of the past which call to him and ask him what will happen to him in the future? For one wild instant he dared to dream. Now? Who knows. Carry on like he is and there is every chance that he will die here one day amid the dust and debris of his former life. A poor legacy to leave the friends he has lost along the way?

He longs to speak to someone about his fears, but he hardly knows who to trust.

In dreams he floats in space, untethered by time. His father's face, beaming, beckons him and he rushes into his open waiting arms. He wakes in tears which he brushes away fiercely. Then he reaches for the space beside him in the bed, where I used to be, and finds emptiness.

"I think I've just made the biggest mistake of my life," he confides in his sister, Beth, on the phone.

Why am I not standing right beside Jim? I really need to hear this.

I am lost in the smoky vortex of a late night party, buried beneath the cushions on a settee at a friend's house. Smoke catches in the back of my throat and I wash it down with vodka, but it does nothing to appease my pain.

I trail home, silent as a ghost, through deserted streets.

Sitting on the doorstep, wearing my black dress, fiddling with the strap of my shoe, I am a love story with no happy ever after. I am everything my mother ever disliked about my hair. I am my father's ruined dream of becoming a writer. I am my grandfather's fist which long ago made an unscheduled appearance through the back door of our home.

The stars are uncaring diamonds, scattered in fistfuls, shunned by heartless lovers. When I turn and step inside, the silence is palpable.

Jim and I still see each other. We cannot help it. We do our best to remain just friends, but inside I ache with longing for him. Every time he leaves me at the door, I want to pull him close to me. The pain of seeing him explodes inside me. I should stop, I really should. He is wrecking my chances of happiness with anyone else. Being with him is like a drug and I am truly hooked.

He doesn't look at all well. His complexion is a strange colour and his eyes increasingly jaundiced. When I mention it, he dismisses my concerns.

"I think perhaps you ought to see a doctor," I begin. How I long to take his hand or kiss him.

He shakes his head.

"They won't do anything. Besides, I'm just tired, that's all."

He is barely eating. We go for a coffee, but he declines a cake. Sometimes his tummy is swollen. Other times he has a slight pain, under his right rib where he rests his hand. He never complains.

Let me look after you, Jim, I implore him silently with my eyes, but I will not tempt fate by speaking my desire aloud. This flickering miracle of connection may be all that I can hope for.

Summer waxes and wanes, impossibly beautiful and fleeting. I can no longer trust love. Jim's greatest gift to me is cynicism. I launch myself into a new relationship, but I know I will bail out before it can flourish. I daren't risk exposing my heart to anyone else.

I see Jim in a crowd, with another woman. I remember her from a previous party, gazing at him. My heart sinks. My suspicion that he was seeing someone else was correct after all. My new boyfriend charges up to me and scoops me up in his arms. I am laughing but I am dying inside.

Now Jim catches sight of me and looks as if he has lost something forever.

He rings and asks to see me. His voice betrays his nervousness. We meet in the chilly sunlight of a September afternoon.

"I still love you," Jim declares gruffly.

I say nothing.

"I know I don't deserve you," he continues, "because I've behaved terribly, but I want to ask you if you would consider giving me another chance. I promise I will never let you down again."

He looks relieved. His face relaxes now that his secret is out.

"I don't think I can," I reply, sadly.

He nods, squeezing my hand.

"That's OK. I expected that. I deserve it, I know. I brought this on myself. I just want you to know how sorry I am. I think I'm going to regret it for the rest of my life."

I eye the white clouds sailing by on a vast expanse of blue sky. The brittle brilliance of the sunlight is turning the pavement slabs into gold. It is as if the whole city is waking up after a spell. I dare to look into his eyes at last.

"For what it's worth, I love you too. I always did. You know that."

"Thank you. Thank you for telling me that." He pauses. "I was so scared of admitting I love you, even to myself. I've spent my whole life trying to block out my feelings. To be honest, they terrified me. But the truth is I loved you right from the start." He gazes at me.

"I'm just glad that I could tell you. I really hope we can stay friends. I'll always be here for you, if you ever change your mind. Either way, I'm going to sort myself out. I've got an extra job. I'm going to get my debts cleared within the year, then who knows? I might even get to make something of myself at long last."

He laughs, a little hollowly, but it is clear he is determined. He is calm and dignified, even in defeat, and I am silently willing him to succeed. He is a remarkable man.

We walk home together, gentle with each other, mindful of what this has cost us both. I kiss him on the cheek. A fleeting butterfly kiss. He smiles warmly at me and I turn and walk away.

Sometimes you get to dictate how a story ends. Other times, you have to sit with it and let the story figure itself out, to let meaning emerge from loss.

I decide to give Jim a second chance which he seizes with both hands. For me, now, he is no longer on a pedestal. He was, and remains, the only man ever to break my heart but I want him so badly. I pull him towards me and push him from me, tormented by indecision. Still it pulses between us, that dreadful, unanswered question to which only he can reply. I wait patiently, biding my time, but I know it must come.

One evening, cosy from the fire, lulled into a false sense of security by Bizet and wine, I broach the subject.

"Jim, I'm only ever going to ask you this question once, but you have to be completely honest with me because if you're not, then it's over forever between us. I need to know if you were seeing that woman while you were with me?"

He freezes, hesitates for just a fraction of a second, then breathes deeply before saying, "I was, yes. But she was... she was with someone else. He didn't know."

Fury seizes me. "I knew it!" Slamming my glass down, I grab my coat.

He rushes towards me. "Please wait. Let me talk to you. It was all over ages ago. Oh, God! I knew this would happen!"

I am on fire, spitting with rage. I cannot believe that all this time, for months, I knew the truth and still he denied it.

"It wasn't how you imagine. Honestly. It was never more than a fling, we both knew that. Her husband never knew. We split ages ago, but she couldn't handle it. She made it obvious she was going to cause trouble." He is shaking, visibly upset.

I am gone. I am flying down the road. I do not care about the traffic. I am raging against the night. I am one of those people you hear yelling in the street. Windows open, faces peer out. I do not care.

He has flung himself downstairs and has left the front door wide open. He is chasing me down the street, breathless and distraught.

"Please listen. At least let me walk you home."

I am gone. I leave him standing in the road, staring after me and I never look back.

I asked for the truth. The whole truth and nothing but. I got it and now I cannot bear it. I am too angry even to cry, too hollow to speak.

Back in his room, Jim hangs over the basin, shaking with remorse. He did the right thing. He was honest. He offered himself up to the truth but it crucified him for his efforts. He puts his head in his hands and weeps, silently. No music can block out his feelings now. He told the truth and shamed the devil. Whatever hold his one remaining secret had over him, it has relinquished its grasp now.

Early the next morning I go to see him.

"You were right to tell me," I say, gently.

He looks relieved. Clearly he has hardly slept. "I kept a diary. I wrote it all down. Here, you can see it. I really love you." He produces his words as tokens of affection and places them in my hands. "Anyway, it's done now. I'm always going to be truthful from now on; it doesn't matter anymore what happens." He eyes me wistfully but makes no claim on me. He means what he says.

I lean toward him and hold him in my arms.

"You did the right thing. I'm proud of you."

I kiss him gently on the lips.

"I don't know what will become of us now," I admit, "but the truth is, I don't want anyone but you."

We walk together by the sea while the waves pound the beach. I have the strange sense we have always known each other, he and I.

To truly love we must be willing to risk the fear that it may all go wrong. There is no other way in the end. I tell him so and he agrees. The path ahead of us is far from easy, but it is a call neither of us can resist.

Thawing out indoors, we stand together, wondering what the future holds. In the mirror, we gaze at our reflections, then look away.

PART 6

CHAPTER 35

It's not always done with roses, on one knee.

My parents are not quite sure how they arrived at the point of marriage.

"Well, one you must have suggested it!" I push them, amused, glancing across at Jim.

"I never mentioned it," my mother declares.

"Me neither," Dad agrees.

"Mind you,"concurs my mother, tartly, turning to me, "I was married to him twenty-four years before I even got an engagement ring!"

This is true. Unable to afford one at the outset, my father made up for it belatedly.

Not that my mother is complaining. "I always wanted a solitaire," she declares, eyeing it with satisfaction. "See, Treasure, it was worth putting up with you all these years, after all!" She has a twinkle in her eye as she says it.

My dad winks, unperturbed.

"Of course my ring is only second hand," he adds.

"It's true. It's even older than your father, Lou!" Mum laughs. "It dates back to 1910 according to the jeweller we bought it from."

"It was probably worn by a World War One hero," My dad announces, puffing himself up proudly as if taking the credit by proxy.

"Well, if your army record is anything to go by, it probably went through the war in a purely administrative capacity!" I grin.

My father made it a point of honour to tailor his army service to suit his own ends. He scowls and turns to my mother. "Remind me again why we had a daughter?"

Jim and I would never be so vague and noncommittal about love, I think, smugly.

Shaking him awake the next morning, I announce I would like a cup of tea.

"Well, you know where the kettle is!" He starts. I groan and he promptly goes back to sleep.

"Hey, you! I want to talk." I prod him. "I'm bored."

He gives in and props himself up on his pillows. "I'm surprised you didn't say everything you had to say last night. You went on for long enough!"

"What do you mean?" I am genuinely puzzled.

He laughs, good-naturedly. "You were talking in your sleep. At one point you said to me, 'Go and check, it's in the wardrobe if you don't believe me,' and like a fool I nearly looked, but the next minute you were snoring again!"

I pat my hair thoughtfully. "At least I have plenty to say of interest."

"You can say that again, chatter-face."

I swipe at him with the pillow but he grabs my hand and pulls me to him and we burst out laughing.

If all the multigrain Cheerios Jim manages to spill on my kitchen tiles every morning were laid end to end, they would surely cover the Great Wall of China.

"Rubbish," he argues, "the Great Wall of Berlin maybe…"

"It isn't even called that. It's the Berlin Wall," I object, pushing past him to reach the butter, a piece of toast jammed between my fingers.

"Well, it would be Great, if it was made out of Cheerios," he adds, stubbornly, determined to win the argument.

"Certainly it would have made it easier to defect to the West," I grin. "You could just eat your way through."

"Unless the checkpoint guards beat you back with a spoon," he grins, tapping the back of my hand with his.

"Get out of the way. I've got to be at work in five minutes," I object. "Or?"

"Or the world will explode. Now shift!"

Half an hour later, the world mysteriously still intact, I arrive at the office, hair slightly damp where I have neglected to dry it properly.

"God, I look a right mess," I moan

"Do you? Funny, I didn't notice. Why, have you done something different to your hair today?" My colleague smirks sarcastically.

"Ha bloody ha. If Jim ever needs to take a sabbatical I'll let you know! You could provide cover for him, no problem!" I grin. I really don't need this. Not from all directions at once.

Jim and I? We're keeping our heads down. We kind of like the way things are at the moment, so why rock the boat? Our amicable bickering continues and other people mistake it for arguments, but we know it is just our own brand of intimacy. We are comfortable with it. He is a morning bird, up bright and breezy the moment he steps clear of the bed. Me? I take three coffees and much persuasion to face the day. Rather like Linda Evangelista, the super model, I don't get out of bed in the morning for less than a tenner. Well, this is Portsmouth. You have to tailor your expectations accordingly!

"When I get to heaven, I'll be invited straight in," I announce confidently to Jim, eyeing my CV. "I mean, I've worked for the tax office, McDonalds and an accountancy firm. That's the axis of evil in its entirety, surely?"

He eyes me, ruefully. 'Did you just finish up the last of my chocolate biscuits?"

"I might need a bit longer to get into heaven now, mightn't I?"

He nods.

People tell you that the first flush of love wears off the minute domesticity sets in, but in our case it hasn't worked that way. Yes,

I pick up his stray socks, wonder why he can't put the toilet seat back down afterwards, and why he has to cover the entire work surface in crumbs when making toast. Even so, it never detracts from his magic. Jim leaves a trail of chaos in his wake, like a comet surging through the sky, but he's such a one off event, I barely notice his faults.

One Tuesday afternoon, we pick an argument, out of the blue.

"Well, you would say that, wouldn't you!" I counter.

"It's because I'm right."

"I don't want to go on like this anymore."

"Like what?"

"This. Us. It's ridiculous. I want to meet someone I can settle down with."

"Marry me then."

Jim's petulant response to our bickering stops us both in our tracks.

"What did you just say?" I ask.

"I'm serious," he says. "Marry me."

I consider the matter for all of two seconds, then gamely decide to call his bluff. "OK, then, you're on."

It is the quickest argument we have ever resolved. Grinning sheepishly at each other, we are still in shock as we wander back to work.

News of our recent engagement is greeted with a mixed reception from both sides of the border. The Scots are concerned that it will be a mixed marriage with all that that entails, given that I am incurably English, and the English are wary of having a Glaswegian in their midst. This crisis is rapidly resolved by me claiming Irish ancestry on my father's side which appeases the Scots, while Jim endears himself as one of the family by solving my father's computer problems.

"Remind me again why I had a daughter?" My father pipes up, indicating I was far less useful to him than Jim will be.

"Ignore him, Lou." My mum declares loyally. "He can't even get your name right."

I twirl my engagement ring around my finger and smile at Jim.
I am bursting with joy. His eyes shine as he glances at me.
"All right, wife-to-be?" he whispers softly.

CHAPTER 36

Our first home together! I am hardly surprised the sun is out. Who could help rejoicing at such good fortune? Even the Green Lady, who stares down her nose at us from her portrait on the wall, would not begrudge us our happiness. I half expect her eyes to follow me around the room as I make up the spare bed, but Jim laughs and we christen her Suzie Wong and suddenly she is far less puffed up with her own importance. Her gaze softens over time, as if she too is moved by our love.

The kitchen is like a galley on a yacht. We move down its length in single file. I half expect the pots and pans to clatter down in a gale and for the boat to have to right itself but it is only the sea outside our window that is moving. A huge continental ferry sails majestically by, promptly cancelling out the sea view until it passes. Occasionally the hovercraft crosses from the Isle of Wight, looking as if it is about to land on the common but always managing to stop just short of it, on the landing slip.

Jim is the captain and I am his figurehead, leaning out proudly from the bow of our ship. My wish is to bring him good fortune. I dance around him, excited by our new home, trying out the sofa, and walking barefoot across the dense luxurious carpet.

At night, we lie resplendent in the biggest bed we have ever shared, admiring the walk-in wardrobe and the dressing table with a mirror and the velvet-covered chair. There is even a swimming pool, shared by the residents, in the communal garden outside. It is freezing cold in early April but that doesn't stop me trying it out.

How does it feel, Jim, after all you've endured, to be here? To come through the door after a hard day's work and be met with a loving kiss and my delighted face? A hot dinner on the stove, ready for you to eat. Did either of us imagine this, in our wildest dreams?

Friends drop by, admire our room, then flop on cushions to watch a film. Sometimes we take a bottle of wine down to the sea and sit talking, cups in hand, watching the sun set rose-red and gold across the glittering sea.

At a nearby treasure-trove of a shop, I buy everything we need to furnish the flat as we want it. A tubby blue and white china Buddha sits peaceably among the pot plants on the kitchen windowsill. Vanilla and rose scented candles adorn the living room. Best of all, Morocco, the cotton cat has moved in. He is striped green and white, with incredibly long legs and a curly tail. His eyes are black stitching, he wears a permanent smile and has a fine set of whiskers. He is a doorstop really, but we would not disgrace so fine a cat with such a demeaning role so he takes his rightful place beside the fire.

I stand in the kitchen, consulting a flying fish. It is made of red cellophane and curls up in the palm of your hand to reveal your fortune.

"Happiness!" It declares. All the portents are in our favour.

From the kitchen window, I can see the ships sail by. Jim wanders in to find me watching them and curls his arms around my waist and kisses me gently on the back of the neck. I turn and smile and everything is perfect.

I wake up and nudge Jim the next morning, busy with dreams, to tell him.

"Shh! I'm still asleep," he objects, laughing. "Go on!"

It was an army of ducks this time. Who knows what it signifies? Sometimes there are people in my dreams whom I do not recognise yet know – my mother or a friend or the man next door.

Jim shakes his head in bafflement and amuses himself with making up a song which he continues singing as he puts his socks on. Padding through to the kitchen, he makes a cup of coffee.

I recline in bed, like the Queen of Sheba, peering out from beneath the bedclothes, luring him with my eyes. Too soon he will pounce and I will put up a mock fight, but always I let him win. It is life itself, this pulsating rhythm of joy. This dance that has no beginning. May it never end.

Real life interrupts us rudely from time to time, demanding that we show up for work, that we at least make an effort to show willing. Casting aside the bedclothes, we do not take it seriously. Our real business is being in love with each other.

I have to pinch myself from time to time, to ensure I have not slipped, unchecked, between the covers of a fairy tale with a happy-ever-after ending.

We are drunk with happiness. On Fridays we stagger home beneath a beaming moon. We hang delightedly from one another, like a pair of coat hangers. Later we collapse on the bed, filling the room with our laughter.

Just leave us here forever, I silently bid the narrative. Here is just fine. We have everything we will ever need. But time is impatient for us to be on the move. It beckons us ever onward.

CHAPTER 37

Jim has been sat talking with my parents at dinner for over twenty minutes now and has yet to utter the F word. Setting a new record for Glaswegians everywhere, he goes into extra time. I eye the clock encouragingly, hoping that Norris McWhirter will appear in time to make an entry for the next edition of the Guinness World Records. Just then, Jim absent-mindedly spears a particularly tricky roast potato and sends his peas into orbit across the kitchen table.

"Oh, fuck! Sorry!" He grins. I mentally stop the clock. Twenty-one minutes. Not bad.

"Don't worry, Jim. It's saved Kerry a job!" My mother grins, making him feel at home. "It's usually her that ends up wearing her dinner."

"Well, that's if she's not burnt it first!" My father, a connoisseur of my limited culinary talents chimes in.

"Great! Tell you what? Next time you all come to dinner, I'll just stick a sign over my head shall I? Pick on Kerry week. 5p a go. All proceeds to charity."

"Hey, don't knock yourself. You could easily get 10p," my mum laughs, raising her sherry to her lips.

"Ha, bloody ha!" I reply, witheringly. "Honestly, it's one rule for him and another for me. I was never allowed to swear at the table. What is this anyway? Celtic diplomatic immunity?"

It's not like Jim set out on a charm offensive. He was only ever being himself.

"People love me just the way I am," he says, confidently, as if reading my thoughts. "I can't help it!"

"Of course they do, Jim! You're lovely," my mother replies, completely under his spell.

*

"You're really hot," I exclaim, turning over beside Jim in bed the next morning.

"Thanks, you're not bad yourself," he grins.

"No, I mean it." I hold my hand to his forehead. "Look at you, you're shivering. You must be running a temperature."

He shrugs in the half light of dawn. The birds have begun singing and woken us early.

"It's just flu," he sighs. "Maybe I'll take the day off?"

I am relieved to hear him say this, but no sooner do I finish getting ready in the bathroom than he is up and dressed and putting his coat on.

"You're not going in? Seriously?"

"Ach, I might as well. I'll only mope about the house otherwise."

He looks jaded. The whites of his eyes are yellowish and again I notice him clutching his side as if he is in discomfort.

"Don't you go worrying your head about me, I'll be fine," he insists, reaching past me for his keys, kissing me on the lips as he passes.

"At least make a doctor's appointment," I entreat although I have all but given up on him.

"OK, I will."

"Promise?"

"If it will stop you nagging, yes."

The GP eyes Jim closely as he talks. He nods, tuts and mutters, making notes on his pad before examining him further. First, he shines a torch in Jim's ears, then he puts a wooden stick on his tongue. Finally, he coaxes Jim's eyelids gently upwards. "A touch of flu, I would think," he pronounces, spinning his chair back towards his desk.

"Plenty of rest and lots of liquids. You should be right as rain in a couple of days."

Jim follows his advice. Nothing improves. He sweats in the night. He shivers in the day. He is constantly popping to the toilet.

"You sure it's not my cooking?" I ask earnestly.

"Don't be daft. Even you're not that bad a cook!" He bats my concerns away as lightly as a shuttlecock.

A few weeks pass. I recommence nagging.

He is almost embarrassed to be back in the surgery.

"It's my fiancée," he apologises, "she keeps insisting I sort it out."

The doctor raises an amused eyebrow. Truth be told, Jim is one of his favourite patients. He can at least have a decent conversation with him. Jim eyes the nature posters of sea birds that line the surgery walls.

"Ah, yes, I'm an ornithologist on the quiet," the doctor confides with a smile.

"No one would ever guess," Jim grins. "Your secret is safe with me."

An albatross hovers over his head – a mobile – as the doctor decides on a routine investigation at the local hospital.

A fortnight later, I go with him. Jim finally goes in and, after twenty minutes, comes out walking like John Wayne.

"That was a bit invasive," he admits when we are alone.

"When do they think they'll have the results?"

He shrugs. "Two weeks, they reckon."

We troop downstairs for a coffee.

If it isn't IBS, I'll eat my hat, I think with smug confidence.

Jim, patient soul that he is, is putting up with my studies of Hamlet tonight. "Do you want fish fingers or chicken for tea?" He asks me, staring inside the freezer.

"Alas, poor Yorick! I knew him, Horatio. Fish fingers, please!" I am attending evening classes in literature and am fixated with Hamlet, now that I finally understand it. Shakespeare was a lost world to me and now I have been granted the key.

"I am in love with Will Shakespeare," I announce contentedly, snuggling my head back on Jim's knee as I lie on the settee to read.

He is very forgiving of my infidelities, provided I concern myself only with sixteenth century bards. He doesn't consider them much competition.

"Tis an unweeded garden that grows to seed, things rank and gross in nature possess it merely," I observe, pointing my Oxford Keynotes towards a window box display where three sunflowers press towards the light.

"Yeah, yeah, whatever," Jim grins as he wrestles with the washing up.

My mother once informed me I would have to date an older man. "A younger one wouldn't put up with your nonsense," she informed me drily.

I stiffen up, dignity intact, and run a bath, one hand still on my book. Then, fresh from the bathroom, I float like Ophelia into bed beside Jim.

"Goodnight, sweet prince, and may flights of angels sing thee to thy sleep," I say, kissing him on the cheek. He groans inwardly and yanks the several yards of duvet I have purposefully wound around me back to his side of the bed.

CHAPTER 38

We are in Glasgow for Christmas.

Beth emerges from the kitchen, tea towel wrapped around her arm, with the roasting tray in one hand and a serving spoon in the other.

"Tuck in everyone, don't be waiting on me. Kerry, have you got enough wine there? Top her up, Jim, would you?"

Six of us for Christmas Day dinner. We pointedly ignore Her Majesty's speech. Nothing she has to say is remotely relevant to Partick. Succulent turkey, pigs in blankets, the ubiquitous sprouts and crispy roast potatoes.

"This is great, Beth," Jim says.

"Yeah, well, after eating at Kerry's, it's bound to seem better!" Vic, Beth's husband, grins.

"Ha, bloody ha! Pick on the English, why don't you? What did we ever do to you?" My red paper hat lurches sideways as I protest.

"Where do you want me to start?" Vic leans forward in mock battle stance.

Margaret is busy chasing a sprout across her plate, but it is putting up a good fight.

"You all right there, Mum?" Beth pats her arm.

"Aye, love," Margaret leans forward and sips cautiously from her daughter's wine glass.

Margaret now suffers from Altzheimer's disease and has moved into a care home recently.

"Cheers, all!" Steven joins in, fresh from getting up.

We are fit to burst by the time the trifle arrives. Margaret stares at it with excitement in her eyes like a little girl at a birthday party. I wonder if she really knows why she is here today? Then, unprompted, she excuses herself from the table and attempts to walk directly through the kitchen wall.

"What are you doing, Gran?" Steven enquires.

"Did you want the bathroom, Mum?" Beth takes her arm and guides her towards the hallway.

She re-emerges moments later.

"She's thinking she's back at West Princes Street," Beth offers, by way of explanation.

Someone has indeed shifted the parameters of Margaret's life. She shakes her head, lost in a snowstorm of confusion, trying to establish what has happened just when she recollects where she is. She isn't quite sure who all these nice people are, gathered around the table, but they seem a lively lot and it was good of them to come and see her. Take the polite dark haired man chatting on the settee next to her right now. She smiles at him, though she really has no idea who he is.

Jim's eyes mist over as he talks gently to his mother, eager to trigger some memories for her. Lucy, the new dog, who replaced her beloved Trixie and who lives at Beth's now, prods his knee, desperate for a fuss. Her doleful eyes are a welcome distraction.

Beth doesn't recognise the blouse her mother has on. It has navy blue polka dots and a long silk tie. Suddenly it dawns on her that Grace, her mother's neighbour at the care home, owns just such a blouse. She wonders privately what Grace's family will make of Margaret's modest attire. At least her mother has managed to keep hold of her own coat this time.

Margaret went to church regularly until recently. She never missed a service. Sometimes she would often arrive the night before the Sunday service and would wait in her usual pew for the minister to arrive. He would sit chatting to her, having already summoned Beth to fetch her home.

Then Margaret grew restless. She would walk around the park at night, Lucy bounding along at her side, hardly safe, out there alone in the centre of Glasgow.

Now that Margaret is tucked up safely in the care home at nights, everyone can rest a little easier in their beds. Only Lucy remains restless. She perches on a windowsill at Beth's house, perpetually searching for her lost mistress but she can be distracted – chasing Pippin the wee terrier, harassing the cats, growling at Vic's slippers and tormenting Steven until he hurls her onto her back and tickles her stomach to within an inch of her life.

Margaret's face is smiling now. She is far away in happier times, long ago. Her beloved Hugh is not far away.

CHAPTER 39

"Hi, how did it go?"

I plonk down on the seat opposite Jim in the upstairs café and plant a kiss on his lips.

"I need to talk to you," he begins gently. He looks hesitant.

"You OK?"

He nods but looks distracted, fiddling with the edges of his jacket sleeve.

"What did the hospital say?"

He has been going for tests for ages now because he is forever going down with flu, shivers and upset stomachs.

"I reckon it's IBS. Am I right?" I demand, cheerily sipping my coffee.

He shakes his head.

"They told me I've got a virus. It's called hepatitis C."

"Oh. What does that mean exactly?"

"They're not altogether sure. They decided to test for it last time I went and it showed up on the results today. Nobody seems to know much about it."

"Still, it's better they can put a name to it, I suppose?" I am insufferably optimistic. I just want Jim to get well so that we can carry on our life together.

He sits thinking for a moment.

"They've said it's not good. Apparently I've had it for a long time – twenty or thirty years they reckon. It starts to attack your liver, left unchecked."

"Oh." This sounds more serious. "What does it mean, long term?" He reaches over and takes my hand.

"The doctor said I could keep going for ten years. Or, as he put it, you could end up under a bus tomorrow, so why worry?" He smiles, attempting to make light of it for my sake.

"Oh, Jim!"

"I'm so sorry," he looks utterly devastated.

"Why? It's not your fault. Besides, we'll get you through it. Ten years is long enough for them to come up with a cure, isn't it?" I squeeze his hand and stare out at the shoppers on the pavement below.

He looks relieved. "I was really worried," he admits.

"Course you were. I would be. It's not an easy thing, is it?"

"No, I mean, I didn't think you would want to stay with me once you knew."

"Jim McPhail!" I laugh, gently, partly shocked, partly disbelieving. "I'm sorry to disappoint you, but you are officially stuck with me. You have to keep going out with me until you bloody well start to enjoy it!"

He loosens up a little and we grin at each other. We down our cups and return to work. What else can we do?

At home I run my fingers through his hair, leaning in to breathe the scent of him that I love so much. He settles down on his computer and does a bit of research. It is unsettling stuff.

We need to ensure we do not share razors or toothbrushes.

"Or Maltesers," I calmly inform him, straight-laced, reaching into a packet.

We blithely separate everything out in the bathroom and continue kissing. That, at least, is not banned.

At the back of my mind is the suspicion that this will affect the question of whether we have children. There is no good time to bring the subject up.

I open my mouth to speak, just as the telephone rings. It is Beth. It is the call we have both dreaded.

Margaret has died.

Jim is standing in the hall, receiver in hand. His face is crumpled and distorted with pain. I take the phone from him and throw my arms around him while he sobs on my shoulder. How much more is the poor man expected to take? The news comes the day after his diagnosis. Did he go through years of fighting only to endure this fresh hell?

I put the kettle on. I run him a bath. He is exhausted. By early evening, he has retired to bed. I look in on him, gently kissing his forehead. I let him talk. Poor Margaret, she didn't have much of a chance in life, did she?

*

The days are bleak and grey. It is snowing heavily in Scotland and freezing cold on the train.

"Passengers passing through Carlisle are requested to take care as we have received reports of bricks being thrown at earlier trains," the guard announces, dourly.

We get free coffee because of the delay, and bricks thrown in for good measure. Good of the vandals to stand out there in this weather. Not everyone would bother.

Why is it that only funerals bring families together?

I meet Jim's sister, Kay, again. Her husband Drew is tall, gangly and thin, with the hard-wired face of a man who has had to fight his way through life. His fingers are stained yellow with tobacco and however hard he tries to smoke his troubles away, their presence never leaves his eyes. His son, Alec, is bright eyed and handsome, restless and friendly, like his mother. His brother, Derek, and sister, Wendy, stand beside him patiently.

They spill into Beth's flat, the enforced reunion managed with amazingly good grace.

Jim and I sleep in Steven's room while he sleeps in the lounge. It is only six weeks since we were here for Christmas.

The next day, we view Margaret in her coffin in the funeral home. She lies there, waxen and perplexed, as if she had a point she wanted to make before she ran out of time. It hits Jim with a jolt, seeing her lying there. He is incensed at the injustice of a life that held so much suffering.

"At least your mum's at peace now," I murmur, my arm in his. The platitude is vastly inadequate but I do not know what else to say to him.

Privately I think that in getting out, Margaret had the right idea. Especially with the weather like it is. The driver continues with tortoise-slow precision as he persuades the funeral car towards the cemetery. Snow is banked high on either side of the lane and it feels as if the whole world is in slow motion.

We freeze in the chapel. We don't know the words of the hymns. The minister makes a valiant attempt to rescue Margaret's life from obscurity, but he gets tongue-tied and mistakes me for her daughter instead of Kay. I want the ground to open up and swallow me, but I must wait my turn.

Death is not just the gradual disintegration of matter. It is the disintegration of everything that ever mattered. Our lives are suddenly revealed in a truer light – brief and insubstantial.

"That's Dad's old Box Brownie!" Beth exclaims, delighted, days afterwards, by her discovery of the camera.

"Looks like there's still a film in it!" She hands it to Jim who examines it tenderly.

"You keep it," she says.

So he does. Later, on the train home, he raises his eye to peer through it, perhaps seeking a window through which to glimpse the elusive past and to search for his father. Then, returning it to its case, he stares out of the window at the hills and farmlands, the remnants of the snow still visible on them, rising from the early morning mists. Margaret is restored to her beloved Hugh at last. Whatever may lie beyond, their love remains untrammelled by the years. Time, try as it might, could not diminish it.

CHAPTER 40

My Irish Nan knows the secret to life. She is eighty-three and hedging her bets, confident that the answer lies midway between Catholicism and a dead cert in the two thirty at Kempton Park. She is busy poring over the racing pages when Jim and I arrive at her west London flat.

She still takes time out to smell the roses. They bloom gloriously on the window boxes on her balcony. Taking Jim's arm, she steers us both through the French doors and on to the patio to see them.

"See that Richard Branston?" She nudges Jim, referring to the Virgin Boss.

"I am familiar with him, yes," grins Jim, while I ponder pickle labels and smile at him.

"He lives right opposite me in that big white house there," Nan informs him.

We gaze out at the mansion, with its white pillars, secluded by oak trees. It is entirely possible of course, but what I find infinitely more fascinating is the factory to our left.

At 4.30 p. m. on the dot, dozens of Bangladeshi women in peacock-bright saris spill out onto the pavement to await collection by their husbands. Tiny birds of paradise, strutting their stuff in the desolate backwaters of London. They should be surrounded by beauty, not pollution-ridden buildings with metal bars at the windows. The humming bird whir of their sewing machines barely solves the mystery of how they washed up here from so many different shores.

The proprietor of the betting shop is Chinese. He tries valiantly to pull the wool over Nan's eyes, but she is having none of it. She duly extracts her £10 winnings from him and goes on her merry way. A bright eyed bird, she is up with the lark every morning, singing songs of old Ireland as she pegs out her washing. Sparkling with memories of long ago.

She loves Jim to bits, my Nan. Her eyes twinkle when she meets him, spotting at once a kindred spirit, a co-conspirator. To the rest of us she remains resolutely awkward and unyielding but that is exactly what we love about her and she knows it.

My nan always looks beyond appearances. The Hungarian refugee who lives next door to her suffers ferocious attacks of paranoia, often accusing the neighbours of spying on him. While they are intolerant, Nan is forgiving. When a fire ripped mysteriously through his apartment, she touched him with her kindness. She was the one who took care of him. She would give her last penny to help an ailing soul.

Upstairs, the teenage drug dealing continues unabated. Nan shakes her head sorrowfully. "I used to feed them bread and jam when they were nippers," she notes, "and now they're banged up often as not."

Years ago, Nan tells us, she lived by the sea and took in lodgers to make ends meet. She warms to her theme, primly tucking her skirt beneath her and pouring Jim a cup of tea.

"One morning, when I was preparing breakfast for them all, I caught sight of a sailor in his cap and uniform at the table. And do you know, no one had any idea at all how he got there!"

She twinkles naughtily, leaving us to guess the rest. Life has yet to defeat my Nan. Twice widowed and bereft of her only daughter, she has taken everything it threw at her and hurled it back tenfold.

We wave energetically long after Nan is out of sight. Turning the corner onto the Harrow Road, we see her again, leaning over her beloved balcony, watching us vanish slowly from view. What must it be like, I wonder, to be old? To see everything recede before you?

And suddenly, she too is gone. In June, a stroke blazes through

Nan's brain and leaves her bed-bound in a London hospital. I see her for the last time the night before she dies. She has been unable to talk for months, yet when she catches sight of my parents and me, she sits up animatedly.

"How are you all?"

We are staggered and delighted, our faces smiling. Then, as if the effort to rally has proved too much for her, she sinks back on her pillows, thoroughly spent. Resisting my mother's gentle efforts to administer a cup of tea, she clutches my hand and grips tightly.

"It's OK, Nan, honestly. You know, don't you? It's no good anyone else telling you what to do, is it?"

She squeezes my hand in acknowledgement. It is the sweetest of farewells.

Life is transitory. Brief, beautiful and fleeting.

The swirling, brushed gold leaves flying about the gutter outside would tell you as much, if you cared to pay attention to them. She couldn't face another winter. Who can blame her? The memory of the sun was forever in her eyes.

In death, she resembles a child again. Her face is lit up with joy, her hands crossed around her rosary beads. Still wondering if Tyson went down in the last round, or whether Rainbow Prince made the 2.30 on a photo finish.

Were they all there, waiting for her? Her long lost daughter Angela, her beloved first husband, her cousin Jackie?

She is only playing at being dead, surely? Any minute now, she will elbow me in the ribs. She will laugh, enjoying the joke.

I bend to kiss her forehead, startled at how cold it is. Deeper than any cold I have ever experienced. I am certain that the body is a shell we leave behind. What animates us while we live?

I feel deeply protective towards my parents. My father is quietly vulnerable at his mother's death. I manage not to cry all day until, finally back at her flat, I sink down into the old green armchair and turn, expecting her to be there. I discover suddenly and sharply that she is gone.

CHAPTER 41

Occasionally Jim catches me peering into prams or admiring wobbly legged toddlers in the park. Shortly after my Nan dies, I am consumed with deep longings for a baby. The intolerable unfairness of grief is prompting me to tip the scales in favour of life. Jim is not so sure it is a good idea. His prognosis remains uncertain. He does not want to die young and leave behind a child.

I, of course, do not have hepatitis C. If I were to conceive, would there be a risk? No one seems able to say with any certainty.

"The odds of you contracting it through intercourse are extremely low," the GP advises. "However, if you did contract it, then there is a potential risk of passing it on to the baby during childbirth."

Case closed. I cannot take the risk, however slight. It is not mine to take.

I start to push the dream aside. Plenty of people don't experience true love, never mind have a child. I am acting spoiled, demanding a baby on top of everything else. Jim is healthy at the moment, surely that is enough?

Jim's hospital appointments increase. The medicines on the shelf at home multiply. Everything, it seems, is procreating. The irony is not lost on me.

Jim is referred to Southampton General Hospital in 1997. A new consultant there specialises in viral hepatitis. It is our immense good fortune that Jim is lucky enough to start treatment under him. He explains the treatment plan in detail and at last we begin to understand what we are up against.

Jim is recommended for treatment with a drug called interferon. Whether it will clear the virus from his system is touch and go, but it is worth a chance.

Interferon comes at a price. Jim's GP leaves us in no doubt that the Conservative government would rather he did not prescribe it and admits that he is forced to adopt half measures solely on the basis of cost. This means that Jim must share his prescribed dosage with another man in Portsmouth. We do not know who he is, of course. Would it help to know? So far, Jim is alone in this battle. We do not know anyone else who has hepatitis C. We know next to nothing about the disease.

"You'll need to keep a strict eye on Jim once treatment starts," advises the doctor. "The side effects can be very severe in some cases."

He is not kidding. Closer inspection of the accompanying information reveals that they range from mild flu to suicidal feelings.

The prescription arrives. Jim, who has fought tooth and nail never to inject drugs again, is forced to return to doing just that. The drug comes in an injectable pen that he self-administers. It is a sobering experience, bringing into sharp focus how he mistreated his own body in the past, injecting into his feet and groin when the veins in his arms failed him. How does an addict become so oblivious of himself as to perpetrate such atrocities on his own body? Jim is not alone. Addicts are even known to inject into their eyeballs if hard pressed and there is no other way.

I stare at him admiringly in the mirror as his arms encircle my waist. I wonder what reflection he saw all those years ago? Surely not the brave incredible soul I see now?

I pat my tummy.

"Oh, I'm fat," I wail.

"No, you're not, you're lovely," Jim consoles, soothingly. But I am tubby. I want to comfort-eat because I am upset that he is ill, that there is nothing I can do to turn the clock back.

I smooth the round curve of my abdomen, contemplating what it would be like to carry his child.

Nature doesn't care what happens to us. Nothing thwarts its progress. Look at the weeds, forcing their heads up towards the sun, between the spaces in the bricks on the wall outside. The baby birds, fat in their nests, greedily squawk to their mothers for grubs.

It will be all right, Jim, won't it? Nothing will happen to ruin us? Not now. I leave these questions unspoken.

Two weeks into his treatment, Jim is sitting reading in the lounge, while I am busy in the kitchen when I hear an almighty crash and I race through to find him bent low on the carpet.

"Oh my God! Are you all right?" Already I am rehearsing emergency procedures.

"It's OK," he looks up, smiling sheepishly. "I just knocked the bookshelf over because I reached out too far from my chair. Sorry."

My relief is such that I cannot even find it in me to shout at him.

Hepatitis C. If I picture it at all, I am instantly transported back to infant school, to a picture poster alphabet that spanned the classroom wall. The one we were forced to recite every day. Now I know my A, B, C...

The C word.

The unspeakable, hated C word.

The worst swear word in the box.

It isn't up there with the A listers, hepatitis C. You won't find a coterie of actors and singers raising funds to combat it. It is, nevertheless, far more prevalent than HIV/AIDS.

Hepatitis C is just the start of the trouble. It's what it leads to, unchecked, that spells disaster.

We are caught between a rock and a hard place. So little is known about Jim's condition currently that we are, in turn, unsure what to tell other people.

For Jim, of course, what is at stake is his past having a negative affect on his present and future employment. He has a history of heroin addiction and a period on remand in prison to consider. Would he be sacked from his current employment if his past were to become known now, even though all of that was long ago, and finished with?

I am anxious too, to protect him from ignorance and hysteria. I cannot bear him being unfairly ostracised by people who do not understand his illness.

"Is there any requirement for Jim to tell his colleagues that he has hepatitis C?" I pursue the question with his medical team.

They shake their heads, firmly. The matter is decided then. Unless we are asked outright, we will volunteer no further information.

I work on the front counter at Social Security. Day in, day out, drug addicts and former users file medical certificates that reveal that they have hepatitis C. Some of my colleagues make explicit and veiled comments about how it would be better for all concerned if they "got on and overdosed." I burn with indignation, for them and for Jim. But mostly I burn with shame because I do not speak out in their defence, because I am afraid for him.

It is an uneasy truce. He is desperate to protect me from intrusions into our private life. Nobody asks us outright and so we tell no lies. Jim has a virus which is attacking his liver, I advise people. They nod politely and assume that I am making a veiled reference to alcoholism and am merely too polite to say so.

On Jim staggers. On interferon he gets weaker by the minute. His eyebrows fall out, making him terribly self conscious. His muscles never stop aching yet on he goes, never a word of complaint. He has little or no appetite although his abdomen is strangely swollen. Several weeks in, he returns to hospital for blood tests.

"I'm afraid there has been no improvement," his consultant states gently, almost as disappointed as we are.

PART 7

CHAPTER 42

We turn and face each other. Neither of us is prepared for this, not really. How can you prepare for something you will only ever do once in your life, if you are truly serious about it?

Butterflies swarm in my stomach as I stand before him in my pale cream dress. Will I do? A pale, imitation bride who has hardly slept for excitement. In me, and he knows it, is a tomboy, climbing trees in the woods of long ago. A dreamer, lost in a story. Tell me about you, Jim?

In my beaming bridegroom, I see a boy, yearning to be loved. A lost young man, torn apart by tragedy. A man who fought heroically against the odds to be here today.

We exchange rings, trembling and emotional. Your tenderness is a sweet shock compared with the tough front you still present to the world. Your eyes are moist. We smile encouragingly at each other, touched by our own transparency.

Our friends and family sit behind us, silently applauding our love, but we alone are privy to its tender depths.

Afterwards, in the spring sunshine, our married life begins with bells and daffodils, with Morris Men who dance splendidly up the High Street outside the registry office, making us suspect they knew we would be here.

Our bond is not contained within registry offices or streets. Our marriage day is beautiful and perfect, but it is as nothing compared with our love.

We were forged in affliction, you and I, our roots entwined a long way back. We are twin souls, destined to collide.

We glide through the night on the train to London. I lie in the hotel bed, thinking not of England, nor of Scotland, but of you. I watch you with tenderness, thinking just how far you have come. You rest your head gently on my chest and I hold you to me, tender as a bird, sheltering you beneath my wings. For all that, you are a still wild thing. Your eyes flash with pain that even love would struggle to erase.

Nothing can destroy us, Jim. We are standing in victory at last. Our match was made in heaven. Did you ever doubt it?

"Good night, Wife!" You beam, throwing your arms around me.

"Good night, Husband!" I nestle into you.

Our perfect wedded bliss lasts for almost an hour until our battle for the duvet resumes.

We are on honeymoon. I sit eyeing half a raw egg yolk, still in its shell, on top of a quarter ounce raw beef burger on my plate, while Jim laughs his head off.

"I thought 'degustation' meant seafood," I explain in bewilderment, wishing fervently that I had studied the menu harder.

"My beef casserole is lovely," he teases, swooping his fork down onto a scalloped potato, before pinching one of my chips instead.

Luckily the waiter comes to my rescue.

"Les Anglais, eh?" He tuts and grins, amused as Jim is, and whisks my plate away. He returns, seconds later, having heated the burger under the grill and fried the egg.

"Thank you," I smile, apologetically, and get to work on my chips. I am still a little wary of the burger which remains pink inside. In the end, when no one is looking, I conceal it discretely in a napkin, and pop it in the front pocket of my handbag so that I can dispose of it in a public bin once I am safely out of sight.

A punk band composed entirely of Japanese girls with long socks and shocking-pink hair is playing on a stage at the far end of the restaurant.

"Bizarre, isn't it?" Grins Jim.

"You couldn't make it up," I agree.

We eye each other up over coffee afterwards. He is gorgeous. I spin my wedding ring round and around my finger, still unable to believe it is really true.

"Well, Mrs. McPhail? Are you all set?"

Jim settles the bill. The waiter nods his approval at my empty plate and I try not to flush beetroot red in response. No wonder French women are thin, I think.

Distracted by kisses, we wander down the road together, hand in hand, looking in the shop windows. The evening air is warm and pleasant. Violin music drifts by from a busker up the road and in the distance, restaurants and bars are setting out their tables on the street, ready for the evening shift. Waiters in smart black trousers and white shirts bustle about, opening wine bottles and setting out glasses.

I get the feeling we are being followed, but shrug it off, thinking I am being paranoid. But no. There is the unmistakable sound of paws trotting along the pavement behind us. I turn around in time to see a determined-looking brown mongrel launch himself at me.

"Oh, my God, Jim, do you think he's got rabies?"

But, after snuffling in my handbag, the dog merely yanks out the hidden burger and, treasure retrieved, trots off into the distance to eat his snack in peace.

"You didn't…?" Jim shakes his head in disbelief.

"I couldn't risk it. It was still raw," I explain, embarrassed at having forgotten to dispose of it.

"Les Anglais!" Jim tuts, looking for all the world like a disappointed waiter.

The Venus De Milo could, no doubt, give me some tips on how to look sophisticated in Paris. She manages it with both arms missing, standing on a plinth. As Jim and I walk upstairs inside the Louvre,

I have a bet with myself that she never ordered Tartare Degustation by mistake. Jim snaps a quick photo.

"I wonder why they never gave them arms when they made sculptures in those days," I reflect.

Jim gazes at me in disbelief, waiting no doubt for the punch line.

"What?" I ask, mildly huffy. "I mean, none of them have arms, not on the really old statues, do they?"

"They've broken off, over the years, you numpty, that's why!"

"I knew that," I poke him in the ribs.

"Yeah, right." Jim laughs, squeezing me to him.

The Venus De Milo doesn't care. Arms aren't very this season anyway. She has done more Paris shows than Anna Wintour. She has nothing to worry about. She knows that being cool is rendered utterly inconsequential by time.

Afterwards, reclining in our seats aboard a bateau mouche, we sail along the Seine while on either side of us lovers recline on the banks. Gazing upwards, I admire the contours of the bridges, gilded by the late afternoon sun, as they arch over us. Even the pigeons ascend with a grace they lack on the streets.

*

But our peaceful odyssey is ruined when a photographer, in search of gullible tourists, clambers on to our boat at a resting place and points a camera in our faces. He is festooned with photographic equipment and winks and grins at us.

"Thirty francs, yes? You like? For souvenir?"

I smile obligingly, ready to pay, while Jim glowers, arms folded against the intrusion. Later, ashore, the photo is hung on a wire fence to dry and Jim retrieves it for me, paying the cameraman who grins in satisfaction.

"Look at your face, Jim! Honestly, anyone would think you weren't enjoying your honeymoon!"

He grins apologetically and plants a kiss on my cheek.

All around us, Paris is bursting into bloom. May Day dawns fresh and clear and we board the Metro to visit the Palace of Versailles. The shop windows are filled with tiny pots containing lily of the valley. Almost everyone seems to be carrying them, their delicate perfume and white bells heralding the summer to come. We stop for coffee in a bakery to discover that even the cakes are decorated with tiny plastic sprigs of the flower. I slip them into my pocket as a keepsake.

Jim has become supremely confident. Marriage suits him. He wears his wedding ring with easy assurance.

Me? I feel like I've received a sudden promotion. I'm not entirely sure I'm up to the job, but I'll be damned if anyone else can apply for it.

"This is the happiest I have ever been in my entire life," I tell him later, lying on a marble stone slab and gazing up at the sky though a mist of trees. We are in the gardens of the Palace of Versailles.

"Me too," he replies, smiling and pulling me up to stand beside him.

*

Dandelion seeds float by on the breeze. I want to reach out my hands and capture them and make a wish that this moment will last forever.

In the central fountain, Neptune rises, trident in hand, with dragons and cupids surrounding him just as they surround Jim and me. The cupids conspire to protect us. Dragons, of course, carry different associations.

I eye the floating dandelion seeds more ruefully. How much are wishes worth in these golden days of our honeymoon?

CHAPTER 43

No sooner are the wedding photographs developed than we receive a request for more pictures of Jim. This time it is the hospital who want to snap him. They are not interested in whether he is smiling or not because they are after pictures of his oesophagus.

"I've got to go for an endoscopy," he says, opening the letter.

"Oh, right. That's where they put a camera on a tube down inside you and take a picture, isn't it?" I ask.

He nods.

My breezy demeanour hides the fact that I myself would be terrified of having it done. I once successfully choked on a Strepsil tablet as a child and have never forgotten it.

"I'll come with you. When is it?"

"Next week."

"They'll probably put you out for it."

He shakes his head.

"I think they just give you a throat spray. It says here it might taste of bananas." He looks bemused.

"Why do they do that, pharmaceutical companies? I bet if you had a poll, banana would come out as the least favourite flavour. It tastes like old socks. I'd make it chocolate flavour. Or orange, at least," I venture.

"Yeah, well, I don't suppose they're too concerned about it tasting like a box of Matchmakers," he grins. "They're more intent on getting results. You haven't thought of becoming a doctor yourself, have you?"

I pull a face. "Too busy right now to fit medical school in, what with doing your washing, your ironing, your..."

"Haven't you got some place you need to be?" He smirks, kissing me as I saunter out the door.

In the waiting room at the hospital, you can tell who is waiting to be seen and who is accompanying them. It is 8.30 in the morning. All the outpatients have rumbling tummies and could murder a cup of coffee. They would rather it was over with but their hopes are dashed every ten minutes or so when a trolley bed is wheeled in from one of the main wards with a whey-faced patient on it whose urgent requirements mean that they will jump the queue ahead of the day patients.

"We'll be with you all as soon as we can." A chirpy blonde-haired nurse appears around the door with a clipboard in hand. "You all right in here?"

Everyone looks up and smiles politely. Then they sink their heads back down into their magazines, or resume complaining about the weather, the government or the lack of decent parking facilities.

Everyone except Jim, that is.

He is busy rehearsing an acceptance speech for his Oscar nomination following the highly successful screen adaptation of his first novel. Not that he's written it yet, you understand, but there's no harm in keeping ahead of the competition.

An hour later, the queue hasn't budged. The blonde nurse appears around the door again, slightly more hesitant but no less bubbly.

"Not long now, folks. Everyone OK in here?"

They murmur assent, but this time in the manner of diners assuring a waiter a meal is just fine when they secretly wish they had the courage to complain about it.

Four hours later, the queue has yet to move. The trolley beds compete with one another up and down the corridor, the porters running a mock Grand Prix when the doctors' backs are turned.

"This is flaming ridiculous," one irate Yorkshire man spouts in disgust. "Four hours!"

Really, it is his nerves talking. He just wants the procedure over with.

I wonder where else he would consider turning for help. Or whether, if he did, it would be provided free of charge. The NHS does indeed have us all over a barrel. Thank God for the NHS. Without it, we would be utterly alone.

Jim returns at 1.30 p.m. having gone in half an hour previously.

"Glad that's over," he announces. He is shaky because he hasn't eaten.

I whisk him downstairs to the canteen.

"Did they say what they were looking for?"

"They want to keep an eye on the veins in my tummy and oesophagus. Apparently, if my liver stops functioning properly, then fluid builds up in my abdomen and it can put pressure on the walls of the veins."

"Is that dangerous?" I ask, eyes widening.

"They say that they might have to consider banding the veins."

"What does that mean?"

"They literally use bands to tie off blood vessels to prevent bleeding."

I nod, taking it all in.

"Still," he straightens up, "they don't seem too concerned about it at the moment. It's just something they're keeping an eye on."

I smile at him and return my gaze to the window, wondering what comes next. I am enjoying the novelty of being married to him and push any doubts about the future away, like a child throwing toys from a pram.

His doctor passes us in the corridor on the way out and stops to chat briefly. He is so proficient at his role that you would be quite forgiven for thinking Jim is his only patient. What must it be like, to be a doctor, really? Can he see further in Jim's story than either of us?

Or is he, like all of us, coping as best he can with the present?

I am never happier than when we are back outside the hospital walls. Jim jostles me down the road, jovial again now that he has eaten. The sun is out and we are Mr. and Mrs. McPhail, newly wed and dazzling, our hearts soaring into the blue summer skies like errant kites that gravity cannot hold down.

Back home, I cook him a pie, in a little heart shaped dish and leave it in the oven. When the phone rings, I ask him to keep an eye on the peas, still boiling on the hob, while I answer it. It is my friend Debbie who can talk for England, but if pressed, can cover Ireland, Scotland and Wales too without batting an eyelid. I gesture frantically to Jim to come and rescue me in five minutes so that the pie doesn't burn.

He duly appears in the hallway, with a tea towel draped over his arm and makes to interrupt me. He doesn't need to. I shout frantically down the phone, "Got to go Debbie! Jim's arm is on fire!"

It sounds the least plausible of excuses but it's true. The tea towel over Jim's arm is alight. He goes to the sink and drops it into the water. Just in time.

"'Sorry about that," he grins sheepishly. "I must have got distracted reading the paper."

"And you ask me why I never found time to go to medical school!" I reply before removing the pie and depositing it upside down on his plate.

Chapter 44

"So what made you decide to come down to England from Glasgow in the first place, Jim?" His new boss enquires, genially.

"Have you ever been to Glasgow?" Jim asks, grinning. "It's fucking freezing!"

His standard reply rarely invokes any further questioning. It's a long story. Where would you start, really, given how busy everyone is?

He gets absorbed in his work, but never insofar as he forgets about the people he works with.

"How is your dad doing now, Sally?" he enquires gently of one of his staff.

"Oh, much better, thanks," she flushes shyly, glad nevertheless that someone has remembered.

"If you need any time off at all, you just let me know, won't you?" He insists.

"I will. Thanks Jim."

He has an uncanny knack of making people want to do their best for him. It isn't premeditated in any way, he is just being himself. For all his charismatic, easy charm, he is as stubborn as a mule at sticking to his viewpoint if challenged.

"Pssst!" He calls over to Lizzie, the blonde clerk who sits diagonally opposite him.

"What, Jock?" Lizzie asks, grinning.

"Did you know that Mike over there wears a wig?"

"No!" Lizzie is shocked.

"S'true. It's a really well made one, I'll grant you. I didn't realise myself until he told me. Go and have a look, but careful he doesn't catch you at it. He's a bit sensitive about it."

Moments later, a small crowd of girls are gathered in a gaggle around Mike who, relishing the attention, is nevertheless bemused. He looks suspiciously at Jim who smiles and shakes his head.

"Popular this afternoon, Mike! What's your secret?"

Mike flushes. "I don't know what you've been up to, Jim, but I intend to get to the bottom of it!"

"Well, put it this way, Mike, I've given you a head start," Jim grins. He reaches forward to answer his phone just as someone tugs experimentally at the back of Mike's own hair, unable to resist the challenge.

As for me, I hate numbers and statistics with a vengeance. I sit fitfully flicking through the accounts on my desk. I cannot concentrate. All around me, my colleagues are engrossed in their work, giving me the distinct impression that there is nothing amiss in the world of accountancy. I would beg to differ.

What are numbers, anyway? They are merely indicators. They are instrumental in getting what you want out of life. They are the targets, the trials and the measures of our tribulation. I begin torturing myself with the thought of never being able to escape from here and resign myself to dying a slow, painful death as the FTSE index plummets alongside me, twenty years from now.

Suddenly, a reprieve. Like a prisoner faced with the parole board, I am fortunate enough to be released to work at a High Street bank instead. On my arrival I am greeted by a rolling bank of TV screens in the foyer that display share prices.

I feel like a market stall holder, offering my wares to customers who clearly know their way around a copy of the Financial Times much better than I do.

"I'm sure that sooner or later they're going to twig that I don't really know what I'm talking about," I confide in Jim, standing hands sulkily in pockets as we queue up for the cinema.

"I doubt it," he smiles "You're an expert blagger!"

I have his vote of confidence at least.

I gaze up at the silver screen. This is more like it, I think, snuggling down alongside Jim as he pops a Minstrel in my mouth.

*

Halfway through the film, having annoyed Jim endlessly with my whispered demands for plot clarification, I realise I must have drifted off. Having closed my eyes, I had dreamed blissfully of a day when he and I do not have to work for a living and we could just be lovers and writers. I am not daft enough to think that anyone would pay us handsomely for either but then such is the case with vocations. At any rate, it beats living by numbers.

Now and then, forgetting we are fighting on the front line against hepatitis C, Jim and I drop our guard and focus on the absurdities of married life.

Right now we are parked in our double bed, in the middle of the kitchen. To one side is the cooker and hob, to our left is the wardrobe, towering and imposing. The only way out of here is by way of the foot of the bed which is pointing towards the door.

"God, I hope they don't take too long fitting that bedroom carpet," I groan, setting off for the bathroom amid a heap of piled up furniture in the hall. "I don't think I could be living like this for long! It's like tackling an assault course."

"Oh I don't know," Jim says, calmly, reaching from the comfort of his pillows for his dish of Cheerios. "I think it could have its compensations."

He selects a shirt from the pile of ironing left on top of the fridge and gets dressed sitting up in bed. He is a master of making the most of things. You would be, too, if you had to live for the moment.

"Well, I think it's like being stuck in prison," I wail, unable to find anything.

"That's what being married to you is like!" Grins Jim, naughtily.

"Oh really! Do elaborate!" I challenge him, hand on hip.

"Yep. Just like prison!" He continues, breezily. "You get kicked awake at 6 a.m. by the warder – that's you, ha ha! – then it's a cold cup of tea in a plastic cup and a bit of stale bread for breakfast if you're lucky!"

He bites into his toast just as my pillow connects with his face.

"Careful," he says, primly. "You'll have crumbs everywhere. The warder doesn't like that, you know!"

CHAPTER 45

"Say that again?" I giggle to my mother, over the phone. "You sound like you're under water! Have you been on the sherry?"

We only got back from a day out in London yesterday, but as usual, I am already bursting with gossip to share with her. Unusually though, she passes the phone straight to my father.

"Hi Kerry, your mum's not feeling too well at the moment."

"Oh no! Sorry. I did wonder. I thought she sounded a bit strange. You both OK?"

"I popped her to the doctors when she got in. She's got a pain in her side. We're just about to take her into hospital."

"To hospital?" I wonder if I have heard correctly. My mother hasn't been near a doctor in over twenty years.

"I'll give you a ring just as soon as we get there and I know more." He puts the phone down.

It is the following morning before I am permitted to see her. Jim and I race up to the hospital together.

"Hi there, how are you doing? You gave us all a fright?" I sit by the side of her bed, tenderly stroking her hair.

"I'm all right, Lou," she says, calmly, eyeing my father as if gauging what to tell me. "I was having a bit of trouble breathing, but they said that my white blood count was very high." She looks bemused at this, as if it had nothing at all to do with her own plans for the evening.

"What do they think caused that?" I pursue.

My mother eyes her wedding ring and pats her bed sheet.

"Now you're not to worry, you promise me, but they think I may have leukaemia."

"Oh, Mum!" My face crumples with shock, even as I make every effort not to show it, for her sake.

"I don't reckon they've got it right, mind you," she whispers confidentially to me. "I mean, why would I get that? I've always been so healthy, eating salads and stuff."

She is, of course, in denial. Who wouldn't be? The absurdity and suddenness of the diagnosis has shocked us all.

A week later, it transpires it is Mantle Cell Lymphoma she is suffering from. Call it what you will, it means that her life is radically transformed. She has trouble breathing and can walk only a few paces before she is gulping in air. Her white blood cells are waging war on her oxygen-carrying red cells. Blood transfusions follow and there is talk of a chemotherapy regime. Her spleen is removed, having grown to many times its normal size as a result of her illness.

"I just can't believe it," I sink down numbly on the settee next to Jim.

He throws his arms around me and holds me tight to him.

"She's going to make it, you know. She's a tough lady, your mum."

"Oh God, Jim, I hope so." I stare bleakly up at him before dissolving into tears.

A month later, we go for a short walk, my mother and I, round the block where she lives. The sun is gently warming the pavements ahead of us, as if willing her to make it. Every few steps she stops still and gasps, lunging at the air the way I once leapt at butterflies with a net, as a child.

"Perhaps we should go back?" I ask her, tentatively.

She shakes her head determinedly and, grabbing hold of my arm, squeezes it to let me know she is not giving up, not any time soon.

Without consciously meaning to, I relegate Jim's illness to second place. I cannot comprehend simultaneously the horrors that both he and my mother are facing. He soldiers on, as the hospital institutes one interferon regime after another. Nothing is working. He goes through months of exhaustion and nausea, losing his appetite and his eyebrows in the process. Each time he arrives for his final check up, he learns that hepatitis C is still rampaging through his body, hell bent on its insidious progress. His resulting cirrhosis is becoming more advanced. He does his best not to worry me. His stomach is swelling up and I chide him to go easy with his diet. Not that it makes sense, mind you. He has never overeaten. Yet his weight is mysteriously piling on.

"I suppose I ought to stop having cakes," he pipes up mournfully, eyeing the tray of shortbread I have just taken out of the oven.

"Oh, one wouldn't hurt, I don't suppose?" I wink. I cannot bear to deny him anything. We have to grab our pleasures where we can. I am learning that fast.

My mother wears a wig now. Her last chemotherapy treatment put paid to the last of her hair. My father sent off for it specially from a firm in London.

"It's amazing, isn't it?" My mother pats it proudly. "It looks just like real hair, you wouldn't know."

I try it on as an experiment.

"It suits you, Lou," she says, admiringly.

"Do you know what?" I say, "I love it. That's exactly how I've been trying to get mine to look for years."

My mother nods, satisfied, while her hairdresser trims the fringe to make it look even more natural.

Later that day, when she is sitting in the hospital, waiting for a blood transfusion, the bald woman next to her says mournfully, "I used to have a lovely head of hair, just like yours, before the chemo started."

My mother leans over and lifts her 'hair' clean off her head and they both burst out laughing. You can't let cancer win. Not all the time.

Jim's consultant is unusually tense as we snake our way along the corridors in hot pursuit of him.

"Are there no rooms available at all in here today?" He pleads with the nurse on reception.

He sits us both down at last.

"I'm afraid it's not good news."

Jim's face drops a little and my heart plummets.

"The damage to your liver from the cirrhosis is getting more advanced. I'm so sorry. We may be reaching the point of considering you for a liver transplant sooner rather than later."

Jim nods slowly. It is not entirely unexpected, this news.

The doctor continues, gently.

"We'd need to do a review and look at certain risk factors. Your age, your fitness, how long you've had the hepatitis as a man."

A Freudian slip, but it's one I can't resist.

"Why, did you not always used to be a man, Jim?" I pipe up, cheekily.

Jim pulls a face at me. The Consultant swings around on his chair, without missing a beat.

"Well, he's been a man all the time I've known him. I can't speak for you, obviously!"

He grins, glad to lighten the atmosphere.

You can't let hepatitis C win. Not all the time, anyway.

CHAPTER 46

"Was I snoring?" Jim eyes me, squarely.

"Course not!" I am grinning even as I say it, because the man next to him is smiling too.

"Good!" Jim convinces himself. He stretches out a little on his train seat and promptly falls asleep again.

Poor lamb. I study his face, its frown line down the centre of his forehead, the tender corners of his mouth where his lips curl appreciably downwards, his nose with its optimistic ending in an upward turn on which he can balance a teaspoon if he thinks no one else is watching and wants to make me laugh. I am consumed with love for him. It is as if I have merged with him, somehow, beyond the physical boundaries that appear to divide us. I know I would willingly endure any pain or hardship, anything to prevent him suffering any more. Perhaps the greatest suffering is in knowing that the choice is withheld from me. I lack his courage. His bravery, and sheer will to endure even the most heinous of hospital procedures, amazes me.

Does he keep fighting for my sake? I suspect he does. I have given him the will to live because I love him so. Is not this, in itself, a terrible burden for him to bear?

He is such a popular man. Kind and generous, beneath that gruff exterior of his. People naturally gravitate to him, but he battles a deep intrinsic loneliness because try as they might, they cannot know what he has endured. The losses he has sustained. He never discusses it with anyone. Of necessity he keeps his track record separate from his career. Would they truly understand, if they knew? Hard to say.

Heroin and hepatitis C are not easy subjects to raise with people who think they know you.

So Jim is partially known to many people. A 'before' and 'after' Jim, neatly book-ended by the demands of the present. A William Burroughs, cut-up method Jim. Exciting, charismatic, different. Everyone thinks they have the inside scoop on him, but they are mistaken. The people who knew him best are long gone.

*

In Glasgow's Anderston, you could have counted the number of Cambridge graduates on one hand and still have a full set of fingers left over. But now they are falling over themselves to talk to Jim. Thank God they are. It is courtesy of their expertise that he is enrolled on a clinical trial that just might save his life. Education, education, education. It's what it all comes down to in the end. That and funding, of course.

Afterwards, we are children, celebrating an early release by the bell. Jim and I spill out onto the High Street to find a café in which to natter. Having dispensed with the serious matter of his treatment, we return to our favourite subject – teasing each other.

"OK, you have to say one thing you really admire about me!" I challenge him, fishing for compliments.

"You have a lovely coat," he replies.

"No! I mean about me!" I continue, rather more seriously.

"Your shoes are very shiny," he grins.

"No, no, I mean something about me as a person."

He sobers up and looks directly at me, smiling. Then, just when I think I have him captured, he shakes his head and says, "I give up! Now I ask you a question."

My shiny shoes collide with his shins beneath the table, even as | I blow him a kiss.

*

My nephew Ben arrives by Stork Express Deliveries the following

April. I hold him in my arms the day he is born and burst into tears of joy. He looks the spitting image of my beloved Irish nan. As if her death had only ever been a spot of larking around and look, here she is right now, posing as a new born baby boy. He is heart-stoppingly gorgeous, fists clenched tightly, one eye firmly shut and dark hair sprouting abundantly from his round head. My sister in law is propped up in bed, looking calm and relaxed as if she performs this kind of miracle every other day. I am besotted with the boy. He and I are joined at the heartstrings. Jim too thinks he is a fine fellow.

At three months old, Ben's little face searches anxiously for his mum and when he doesn't find her, is reduced immediately to a welter of tears. I feel his anxiety keenly and rush to his side as he sits propped up in his reclining seat. I love to hold him and watch him blowing bubbles, big gorgeous boy that he is.

By the time of his christening, next to the little church in the New Forest beneath the summer trees, his legs dangle off the edge of my arms as I hold him. His eyes are transfixed by the dark blue floral pattern on my skirt. He wears a pristine white christening gown he will quickly outgrow. Next summer, those will be *his* feet, prancing joyously up and down in the long grass where now the other children roam.

Jim cannot come to the christening. He is not well today. Nobody here realises quite how ill he is, but I do. He is exhausted, soaked with perspiration, shaking with flu. Interferon is almost as bad as the early stages of the disease it sets out to cure.

It does not matter yet to Ben that Uncle Jim is not here today. Ben does not know what an uncle is or that he has one. He fixes his gaze intently on the church wall, looking for all the world like a solemn old man, who has surveyed the world and found it wanting.

CHAPTER 47

Jim is a big fan of the Surrealists, Rene Magritte in particular. He loves Ceci N'est Pas Une Pipe, the famous painting of a pipe, or, as Magritte would have it, just a representation of a pipe.

We are standing transfixed in the newly opened Tate Modern in London, the glorious cathedral to the arts.

I approach Louise Bourgeois's mammoth steel sculpture of a spider entitled Maman and walk beneath it. It is enormous, commanding the full attention of the audience in the Turbine Hall.

"It's about the same size as that one in the lounge I got rid of the other day," I note airily.

"Not that you're exaggerating of course," Jim grins.

I am shocked. Then again, he knows that my fearless handling of arachnids usually extends to running towards him, hollering and pointing, an expression of sheer terror on my face.

"Look at that marvellous installation over there."

I point sarcastically to a window ledge where it appears that the contractors have rapidly finished painting and forgotten to pack up afterwards. An abandoned coffee cup and paint pot lie on the side, undisturbed and viewed with interest by a number of highly pretentious art students with overactive imaginations.

There are skulls and tribal effects in one room. Monet in another.

"Now Dali, I do like," I announce with satisfaction.

The painting is titled Autumn Cannibalism. It consists of a creature eating itself with a knife and fork. Utterly compelling, horrific and absurd, Dali's talent spills out onto the canvas. This is the measure of great art. Dali's masterpiece, however, attracts only glances from passing students, more absorbed in the laughable constructs of modern day artists with their scorn for artistic skill. Is this an effect of ageing, my adoption of scathing disregard for what is valued in the contemporary art world? How does it creep up on you, this sense of outrage at a lack of reverence for the past? Why should I value Dali above Emin anyway? What do either really represent to me? Yet I am furiously defending Dali's talent. I have no need to. It speaks for itself. He is gone and whatever it was he had to say to us, is painted across his canvases for all to see. The old masters have endured throughout time but modern art is in tune with our ultimate demise. Tracey Emin's unmade bed will surely need to be remade over and over if it is to survive her death. It will subsequently become less of its true artist and more of its intervening curators.

Is it the same with Jim and me? Who will remember us when we are gone and forever changed?

We sit in the upstairs café, gazing out across the millennium bridge and the figures in the distance who hurry across it like tiny insects. I am reminded of those ants of long ago in childhood, poking up between the concrete, sensing a storm. They are gone now, replaced no doubt by other ants, many generations down the line. What is it that we seek so dearly to keep hold of?

Jim has a cappuccino moustache. I move to wipe it off but he play fights me in protest, twirling the ends as if to manifest Dali himself.

All around us, sketching students contemplate the walls. The general public suffer a conceit of pretentiousness or outright amusement at what meets their eyes. I squeeze Jim's side and cuddle him to me. The real work of art is right here. It is love, impossible to forge.

Afterwards in a subway, Jim stoops to offer a man slumped in a corner a few coins.

"Thanks mate. I could do with that."

"No problem," Jim smiles.

The man rises up, shaking newspaper sheets from his coat as if he is indeed a scarecrow stuffed with straw beneath the layers of his jumpers and donkey jacket.

"Now, Sir, you look like a man I may have a conversation with."

"Oh, aye?" Jim enquires without flinching.

The man walks alongside us for a moment.

"You see all these cars parked up on the roads along here?" He gestures to Jim.

"One day, mate, mark my words, they will rise up against us all and take over the world and what will the point of it all have been then, eh?"

He shakes his head disconsolately and smoothes his jacket down as he beams at Jim, ludicrously pleased he has been heard.

"Until then, pleasure to meet you, Sir. We must do dinner together some time, and the wife too."

Jim grins and pats him on the shoulder and we go on our way. The man nods, satisfied, and slumps back down onto the pavement to await his next encounter.

The Hunterian Museum at the Royal College of Surgeons is a rare and beautiful exhibition hall. Glass display cabinets house the wonders of the human body – bones and anatomy, the progress of disease across the human body, the effects of small pox and the ravages of elephantitis. Assorted bottled creatures vie for position alongside human skulls. Jim and I are alternately fascinated and repelled by the contents of the jars. Here, perhaps, most poignantly of all, are quintuplets, joined in a circle, hands clasped, as they lie dormant and underdeveloped in a glass prison. The still born, premature babies of a Lancashire woman in 1786 are heartbreakingly beautiful and macabre, their faces flawless, mouths open, eyes shut against a world that would not let them enter and live.

Who would they have been, had they been allowed to live?

Arrested not only from their own development, but from all the lives that would have sprung forth from them, generations hence.

It makes you question how we happen to be here. Gazing at them, over two hundred years later, one is forced to contemplate the terrible truth that, while they have yet to be forgotten, the millions who lived among them, such a comparatively short time ago, already are.

I squeeze Jim's hand. He does not like it here, among the harsh realities of this silent, clinical world. Half dreaming of his beloved paintings, he saunters over to the surgical display.

Eyeing an endoscopy instrument from the 1800s, he notes, with bitter experience,

"They haven't changed much!"

I feel sick at the thought of all he endures at the hospital. We move on to look at the surgical tongs used to extract Samuel Pepys's infamous kidney stones. Every year in his diary, he would faithfully note the anniversary of the operation and thank God he was not enduring it again.

Perhaps, there is, after all a reason for the grace of the passage of time – the slow, sweet river of regret that urges us onward, with or without our permission.

We slowly move down the impressive staircase and back out into daylight, quietly relieved. Laughter revives us. We pose by Dickens's Old Curiosity Shoppe, where Jim takes my photo.

"Hey, Mister! I know what would make a good photo!"

An excited road sweeper ushers us over. Exchanging my jacket for overalls, mop and bucket, I enter into the joke immediately. Jim is in stitches, taking my picture alongside the vehicle. We shake Anthony's hand warmly afterwards and he poses proudly for a picture too.

"See the wife's got a new job at last?" Jim jokes for days afterwards to anyone willing to listen, producing his evidence with a flourish and enjoying my protests.

*

CHAPTER 48

When I arrive, my mother is in the garden, pegging out washing.
The cats weave protectively around her, and eye me suspiciously until
I bend to make a fuss of them.

"They haven't stopped eating all morning!" Announces my mother,
putting her washing down to greet me.

She tours the garden, showing me the cherry tree blossom and the
hyacinths, the garden pond on which a lily flowers.

"Here, come and see this," she beckons. She pauses by the curry
plant, as she always does, and rubs the leaves into her fingers.

"It really does smell just like curry, doesn't it?" She declares with
satisfaction.

William the cat appears and savagely bites a piece out of the top of
it before scooting off, his tail high in the air.

I revel in these little moments with my mother. I have left Jim at
home to rest, tucked up in bed, still shattered, with a hot cup of tea
by his side.

My mother stands at the sink, peeling potatoes while I drink my
coffee. She won't let anyone interfere with her routine, cancer or no
cancer.

We are nervous, my mother, my father and I, though we do not
admit this to each other. This is the great conspiracy of terminal
illness. It forces you to negotiate a terrible pit into which one of you,
ultimately, will fall.

My mother, of course, knows what she is dealing with. The doctors
hinted at three years from diagnosis. That, to her triumph, was four

JAMES WITH A SILENT C

years ago. Since then, there have been various interventions. Blood transfusions to redress the balance against her warring white cells. Chemotherapy regimes that promised hope, but delivered muscle weakness, hair loss and unrelenting nausea. An autologous stem cell transplant that took my mother to the edge of hell itself.

She smoothes her abdomen down.

"Your dad and I went for a check up yesterday," she begins.

"Yesterday?" I am shocked. "But you didn't have an appointment. It was a Saturday?"

My mum is gentle, taking her time, for my sake.

"They think my tumour has come back." She pauses. "I knew it had, really,"

She indicates her stomach, increasingly swollen on the left hand side. All light-hearted talk of diets is set aside.

"Oh, Mum."

"Oh, now, Lou, it's OK. We knew what to expect, didn't we."

She is so stoic; I cannot disgrace her by descending into tears. I steady my cup in my hand and reach out to her.

"I'm so sorry... after all you've been through!"

She holds me in a brief hug, then we pull back from each other, lest we cry.

Instead we focus on whatever will make the other laugh.

My dad is busy talking about the marines, when Mum pipes up.

"I met a marine once and he had one of those, what-do-you-call-them? Piss helmets on?"

"You mean pith!" Corrects my dad, laughing.

"Oh, yes!" Mum snorts between swigs of sherry. "So I do. It was when I worked at the Landport. I was going out with him and one of the girls didn't believe he was really a marine; she said I was making it up. Ray he was called. So I told him and he got six of his mates to come into the shop, all dressed up, to parade in front of her! She couldn't believe her eyes!"

"Did they all remember their piss helmets?" I tease.

"Ah, shut up," retorts Mum, pulling a face.

"How's Jim?" She asks, gently.

"Not too bad," I reply, breezily.

There she is, my mother, bald as a new born duckling, having lost all her hair on chemo, banned from eating mayonnaise since her stem cell transplant, and yet she finds time to concern herself with everyone else.

"I do love you," I tell her, my voice wavering on the edge slightly. I cough to conceal my emotion.

"Course you do. I'm your mum." She reaches up and squeezes me to within an inch of my life. "Oh you are tall. I wish I was tall," she laments.

"No, you don't. It's nice being tiny."

"But I can't reach any of my saucepans," she wails, eyeing them hanging above the kitchen cupboards on hooks put up by my father.

She is a Lilliputian in the kitchen. I lean over with staggering ease and airily reach for the frying pan.

"Show off!" She says, wryly.

Later she decides to have a clear out.

"Why would you need three butter dishes?" I challenge her.

My mum pauses for a moment.

"I don't, Lou, to be honest, do I?"

I shake my head.

"You have one," she insists. "Pick whichever one you like best."

I look at the pale Bakelite one with the white lid that I remember from childhood.

"Go on, it's fine. You'll be doing me a favour. See that's why I need you here. You're sensible at not keeping too much clutter. Not like me; I'm a hoarder."

We are perched on the cushion-covered rug-box, choosing what to keep and what to give away. The cats, Penny and William, weave in

JAMES WITH A SILENT C

and out of the stacks of plates. Penny, utterly careless of breakages, whips her tail furiously behind her and William paws my knee, demanding a fuss.

"You be good kids," Mum eyes them myopically. How much easier than children they would have been to raise, demanding only food and love. I catch Mum looking at me with a faraway gaze in her eye.

"You all right?"

"Course."

She sets to with a will. Plates next. There are dozens of them. Fruit bowls, spatulas, copper jelly moulds, potato peelers.

I go home with half the contents of her kitchen wrapped in newspaper in carrier bags. She doesn't really want to get rid of anything. No one ever does, truly, do they? I am conspiring with her in keeping it in the family. The terrible dark secret of what we are really doing is left unsaid. We are preparing.

Hard to imagine the kitchen without her in it. I daren't, to be truthful. It fills me with anxiety, the thought of her easy, reassuring presence no longer at the sink, peeling mushrooms and listening amiably to me talking nineteen to the dozen about my latest wild plans.

"Love you!" She says.

"Me too," I reply, kissing her on the cheek.

She waves frantically from the lounge window until I am out of sight.

"What's all this?" Demands Jim, with interest, poking experimentally in the assorted bags on my return.

"Mum was having a clear out," I explain.

He knows. Within seconds he encloses me in his arms.

"It's all right. Have a little cry. Of course you're going to."

In his arms, at least, safe and warm, it cannot reach me. The horror of the end.

Chapter 49

In the spring, one of the baby birds fell out of its nest. We found it smashed and dead on the path outside my mother's back door, its useless, rudimentary wings too underdeveloped to have saved it.

My mother took it to heart. Her old childhood superstitions crept back to life and stole over her like a shadow.

The innocence of her old beliefs, the ones my great grandmother had installed in her, were baffling to an outsider. The fear that bats flew into your hair if you let them get too close to you or that the safest place during a thunderstorm was the cupboard under the stairs. Never, ever were you to attempt to wash anything on New Year's Day or you would surely wash away the luck of the New Year.

Me? I do not believe in superstitions. Neither does Jim. But now, in a back street in Weymouth, I am confronted again with a dead bird, a thrush, lying in the gutter. It is beautiful, its plumage still immaculate. Its mottled chest and dark staring eye are unsullied. It must have been stunned by a passing car. Perhaps, seconds before its own demise, it might have been mid-song, praising the very creator who brought it into being.

I try not to mind, but it plays on my own fears. My mother is far from well now. I am desperate not to burden Jim with my feelings. He deserves this brief holiday, poor love. He has struggled through years of increasingly torturous treatments. What are we to do?

The dichotomy we experience is a harsh one. On the one hand we are careless holidaymakers, enjoying the early May sunshine, but on the other, we are the realists who know that whatever way we chose to paint this scene, it remains inescapably sad.

I gaze at the buckets and spades outside the sea front stores. Day glo windmills whirr in the breeze and exotic shells washed up from far flung shores are displayed in eye-catching baskets. The beach is splendid. An oasis of golden sand, miles long. Ahead of us is Brewers Quay, with its old fashioned sweetshop. I buy candy striped canes and a box of chocolates on which a china swan sails across an ocean of ribbons. My mother can no longer eat the contents, but the box is so pretty I want her to have it anyway. What I really want to buy her nobody is offering for sale, not even the doctors.

I can only sit with her now. I can only offer her my presence, quiet and unobtrusive, by her hospital bed. Every day, after work has finished, I walk slowly up the hill towards the hospital. I wash my hands thoroughly on arrival, patting my face to cool it down from the hot July sunshine. The temperatures have shot through the roof. It is a record summer.

We were joined in life once, she and I. I lived in her and through her. Now I must live for her.

"Oh, Lou!" she exclaims. "You shouldn't be coming to see me. You must be tired."

Tired? What right do I have to be tired? I watch her, hunched over the side of the bed, kidney bowl in hand, fighting the oncoming nausea. Her vast swollen abdomen carrying not a child this time, but a tumour. In her thin cotton night dress, she alternates between shivering and sweating.

I rub my hand gently over the small of her back, trying to alleviate the worst of the pain.

"Oh, that's nice," she exclaims as if in relief but more, I suspect, to allow me to feel useful. She never stops thinking about others, my mum. Not even when she is dying.

Yesterday she looked forever changed. Paler, greyer. The shadow of death had stolen across her features and I knew instantly the fight was all but over. My father became desperate to bring her home, as if her presence in the hospital was really what was making her sick and if we could just get her out into the sunshine, all would be well again.

Of course it wasn't to be. The last fateful journey home has begun. I am touched to the core by how very deeply my father loves her.

Driving away from the hospital he sits now, with one hand on the steering wheel and the other hand gently clasped in my mother's. On past the hedges and fields, past the meadow where she and I used to walk long ago, admiring the horse who stood there and is no more.

The final morning dawns. She watches the wall, her eyes intently following something that her senses can no longer process and we ourselves cannot see. She shakes her head in disbelief, but lacks the speech to give voice to her confusion. At last, we take her back to the hospital, the dream of dying at home gone. Mercifully, morphine sets about its final work. Hours pass in the deadly heat until night approaches. Its soft breath cools the room from the aching torturous sun that tore through the gaps in the binds and gave her no respite.

Nurses usher us from the room, my father, brother and I, then call to us urgently moments later.

"She's fading quickly. Please come in."

Suddenly it is all over. Four years of suffering ends in a trice. A trickle of blood, the last indignity, slips from my mother's gaping mouth. My father reaches forward tenderly, producing a tissue from his pocket, and wipes it gently away.

"Well done, Treasure. You can rest now."

And in that selfless gesture, everything I ever needed to know about true love is captured perfectly.

*

We are dressed in black, sitting perched on the settee at my brother's house, waiting for the hearse. My father, Jim and I. Ben is looking smart in his little jacket and trousers and is playing with the sunglasses his mother has given him.

"Where is Nanny? Is she coming too?" He asks

The awful frozen silence.

"She's coming with us in a special car that will follow on behind," Jim chips in quickly, saving the day.

Satisfied with this, Ben sets to showing me his little toy dog and I teach him how to make a noise by pushing the palms of your hands together.

Inside the chapel, I expect to find Mum already in the pew, waving to us to come and join her. Instead there is only her flower-strewn coffin. I clutch Jim's hand and put my other one arm around my father. It is up to me to take care of them both.

How did they all know to be here? So many old friends, dearly loved.

Mum would have been so touched. The women from Garlands whom she worked with years before, sobbing quietly into their handkerchiefs; her best mate Julie, who feels the loss almost as keenly as we do ourselves.

I am stiff with apprehension, but my father is depending on me. I stand to give the tribute and Jim is with me every breath of the way, willing me on. I can do anything with his gentle eyes watching over me.

"You know that Jim really does love you, don't you?" My mother's voice, a few days before she died, reaches me as I return to him.

I do know, I think. I slip into his arms. He leans over and holds me to him, his pride swelling as he kisses me.

"Well done, you were brilliant."

I cannot speak. I can barely stand upright. But I do not cry. We are focused on surviving the present moment.

*

I turn briefly to look out of the back window, stifling my tears. I am startled to find the road empty. Mum is no longer following on behind in that special car of hers.

The next morning, no one is about. We go to the crematorium to meet Mr. Ensell, who tends to the gardens. He appears, carrying a casket of ashes. Mum, as we knew and loved her, is poured out over the soil. There is a surprising amount of pale grey dust. Powdery remnants from the top of the jar evaporate like fine mist on the air, sending a prayer heavenward to an invisible God.

Mr. Ensell, sensing our shock, gently rakes over the ground. We have chosen this spot because it looks out over the lawns towards a silver birch tree and a weeping willow, like that garden of childhood, long ago. We place roses on the ground and Mr. Ensell pauses, eyeing us all.

"See this here, this is a curry plant," he announces, reaching over and rubbing the leaves onto his fingers. "See? It smells just like curry."

I smile briefly, in spite of myself. I had barely noticed the curry plant, yet now it seems perfectly placed. The sun's rays gently warm us and it is for all the world as if my mother's smiling presence is still with us.

CHAPTER 50

It is Christmas Day. I cannot stand the empty chair at the table that will never be filled. My father, brother, sister in law, Jim and I raise our glasses of sherry to Mum, all of us fronting it out in public, saving our tears for afterwards, in private.

It is agony watching my father's pale hollow-cheeked expression as he bravely puts on a smile for our sakes.

On Christmas Eve, the urge to still buy her a gift was so overwhelming that I chose a Christmas decoration for her. Two jovial snowmen, arms linked, scarves aloft, sitting on a bed of artificial red berries. When the shop assistant smiled at me I wanted to burst into tears. Instead, I went to my mother's place in the Garden of Remembrance and set down the snowmen on the earth where her ashes lay.

Today, we distract ourselves with Ben, the star turn at the table. Next year he will be three years old, but for now he retains his round, baby shaped head and solemn eyes. He sits talking animatedly to anyone who will listen.

"I've done a very silly thing, Auntie Kerry," he pipes up, as I wrestle with my sprouts.

"Have you Ben? What's that then?" I ask.

"Well, I've left my motorbike parked up outside the factory over Christmas."

Jim stifles a laugh, as I reply thoroughly straight faced. "Did you, Ben? How come?"

"Well, I had to go in and do a bit of overtime this morning," he announces. "I've been a bit stressed about work, so I took the bike in and there you have it!"

There you have it indeed! My brother, as amused as the rest of us, raises an eyebrow at Ben's tall tale, strongly suspecting he has decided to copy what his daddy has been up to.

But Ben is as composed as ever.

"Grandad, you know those flats you passed on the way here?" He asks.

"Yes, Ben?"

"Well, I built them."

"Did you?"

"Yep." Ben sinks his cola.

"Did you built that house next door to us too, Ben?" I venture, unable to resist.

"No, Auntie Kerry, that's not one of mine."

Ben humours me but clearly finds the suggestion absurd. He is, after all, only two.

We resort to tickling him and he gurns and giggles in delight.

Now that I have lost my mother, I finally understand the true nature of grief. I find myself crying at inopportune moments; in the street, in the middle of Marks and Spencer, on the bus. I panic, reaching into my pockets for tissues as the tears flow out of nowhere.

"It's OK. It's good to let it all out." Jim sits patiently beside me on the settee, his arm around me. "Don't try to hold it in."

"I'm so sorry,"

"Whatever for?"

"Because I realise now just how useless I was to you when you lost your mum."

"No, you weren't."

He is gallant as ever. But I was. I know now that I was.

There is, of course, the thorny issue of the fact that now I realise that life is not forever. It has finally sunk in that Jim and I will not last together for always. I watch him now with the eyes of one desperate to record every moment, trying to capture the unattainable, to perform the magician's last trick and make immortality a reality.

Days before she died, I caught my mother watching me closely, an intense look on her face, as she stroked my hair tenderly. Now I realise she too was trying to commit me to memory.

On Boxing Day, I return to her grave. Pigeons, mistaking the artificial berries on the gift I left for food, have pecked them to pieces and left the white polystyrene insides exposed like shards of bone.

I put the new calendar on the wall in the kitchen and mark up Jim's latest round of hospital appointments. January rushes up to greet us before either of us are ready. Time, like a river, surges forward, hardly caring whether it carries us with it or not.

PART 8

CHAPTER 51

Quiet and reverential, blanketed in snow and silence, the city sits nestled by the Stour. We are in Canterbury, Jim and I, seeking refuge for a few days. The house we are staying in is silent at all hours, a place of retreat. I am grateful for the chance to rest at last, exhausted from the grief of losing my mother.

The landlord is a strange and solitary man, suspicious of strangers. It is a curious occupation for him, given that he lacks social ease. I begin to suspect he has bodies closeted away in other rooms and joke to Jim.

"I did wonder why the sink was blocked," he grins, turning to me in the middle of washing up.

"Don't even joke about it. I reckon he's got his old mum propped in the next room, talking to her twenty years after she's died," I retort, then promptly fill up again at the talk of mothers.

"Oh God!" I am impatient with myself, reaching for the tissues, anxious not to ruin things for Jim.

He stoops to comfort me.

"It's OK, let it out. That's what we're here for. Shall I make you a nice cup of tea?"

I nod, grateful to him. I have been so caught up with things that I've barely given him a second thought. Somehow he is going strong, shrugging off any suggestion of fuss. We put our coats on and head out, hand in hand, along the river. The ducks waddle up to us across the banks, noisy and domesticated.

"Here," Jim reaches into his pocket, having brought a few crusts of bread.

Ducks can never fail to cheer you. Rotund and argumentative, they peck at one another mercilessly as they compete for crumbs.

The next day my father comes to join us. In the cathedral, we gaze up in hushed awe at our surroundings. It is truly beautiful in here. Not the ostentatious beauty demanded by modern day tourist attractions. Nor the results of the efforts of the clergy, eager to raise the numbers of visitors. Not even the clean lines of architectural excellence. More, it has to do with the quiet stillness. The great swathes of time that have transfigured the past and washed it clean of blood and anguish.

A priest was murdered here, on the spot where he knelt to pray, and ever afterwards the pilgrims came.

Beckett's bones lie in an elusive resting place. Life goes on all around him, but the stillness of the place that marks his demise is tangible. It cannot be trespassed upon, only sensed keenly, only felt.

Outside the cathedral, the grass is verdant, peeping out beneath the snow. Blackbirds criss-cross the lawn, swooping low. A priest sits smoking a cigarette, looking for all the world as if he is merely a costumed guide, hiding from the tourists.

We return to the crypt and light a candle for my mother. The light of remembrance. The flame sputters in the darkness, valiantly attempting to eliminate the black hole of grief that surrounds us. My mother, though, is not found in crypts or darkness. Most likely she is among the moor hens that strut on the river bank between the early daffodils. We cross the bridge and head over to the Westgate Tower.

Inside, we gaze at a soldier's personal effects, laid out in a glass display cabinet. We ponder the person who owned them, long ago, the thought of him made tender by our own dear loss. I am wandering into an upstairs room, dark and forgotten, when the guide appears suddenly in the doorway.

"Oh, my! Look!" Just then, up from the floorboards, appears a Red Admiral butterfly. It flutters up towards the light from the leaded window. Some people think they only live for a day, butterflies, but it isn't true. Sometimes they can even make it through the winter, if they find an attic to shelter in.

I am cast back briefly and warmly into a golden sunlit garden of long ago where my mother kneels to trowel the earth with a fork and I perch on an upturned flower pot, chattering away to her.

Outside, Jim treads carefully around the flowers, anxious not to disturb the new growth. So much loss, so close to home, has made us gentle with each other, mindful always of our own transience. In the end, he will leave me standing here, remembering. From the start, it was always written that way.

How hard to have to turn your back on all of this? The light, the trees, the wordless architecture. Life takes it back from you, eventually. We are merely tenants here.

My father returns home. At least the breath of fresh air has done him good. Dreading the blackness, the bleak feeling that creeps in around the edges of his days, he hugs me tightly to him before he goes. Now, every measure of goodbye contains the memory of that original grief. There are no light, inconsequential partings any more. Everything has become imbued with a deeper meaning.

I turn back to Jim. The fast moving, flowing river signifies life, thrusting forward, undeterred by any momentary sense of loss. In the grand scheme of things we are all connected to a single point. It is only our consciousness, a window that opens fleetingly, that would have us believe it otherwise.

CHAPTER 52

For a moment, I think there is a heavy breather next to me in the train carriage. Jim is puffing in and out, gathering himself after our short run.

"Are you OK?" I ask.

"Mmm. Just out of breath." He pats his tummy, by way of explanation.

"Oh, Jim!" He looks like he is about to burst, I think, as I eye his abdomen dolefully.

"Another mouth to feed," he jokes, trying to cheer me up.

But it is no joke. His tummy is hugely distended now, round and tight as a drum. He does indeed look as if he is in the late stages of pregnancy.

Back at the hospital, even his consultant is alarmed. He races along the corridor, in search of a colleague who can perform an emergency tap to release the fluid build up that has caused the swelling. Unchecked, hepatitis C can cause cirrhosis of the liver and when fluid accumulates in the peritoneal cavity, it can build up to horrific proportions, as we are about to discover.

We sit in the waiting room, awaiting the doctor's return. Moments later we are ushered into a ward and asked to wait. It is tight for space in here. There are so many beds shoved alongside one other that there is barely room between for the dividing curtains that offer a measure of privacy. When the doctor arrives, I slip out to make room for her to attend to Jim.

I stand around awkwardly before looking for a place to retreat to.

Spotting an elderly gentleman sitting on a chair, I make a bee line for him, and sink down gratefully beside him. He beams, reminding me of Steptoe's Wilfrid Brambell. Seconds later, a nurse arrives and draws a curtain around us both.

"Oh, I'm so sorry," I apologise. "I'll get out of your way."

"No, love, there's no need. Provided that this gentleman here is happy for you to stay?"

The nurse beams at the elderly man who nods vigorously in response. Clearly he is revelling in the attention.

"You're family, I take it?" she asks, beginning to help him undress. No doubt she has me tagged as his loyal daughter.

"No, no. I'm... I don't even know him." I flush furiously and, making my excuses, disappear beneath the curtains.

I return to Jim's side.

"What have you been up to?" He demands

"Tell you later," I grin, squeezing his hand. "Any luck yet?"

He shakes his head, eyeing his swollen tummy on which the doctor has daubed tiny crosses in magic marker pen.

"You look like Cool Hand Luke after he ate all the eggs for a bet," I announce.

The doctor, latex gloved, continues to manipulate the needle, searching for the exact location of the fluid. Not easy, without Jim's latest ultrasound scan which has gone missing. Exasperated, she finally concedes defeat.

"I'm really sorry. We'll have to make an emergency appointment and have you back in a day or two."

I nod, hoping that Jim will last until then.

He gets up and pulls his trousers on. His wardrobe consists of five different sizes of clothing now, depending on the levels of ascitic fluid inside him.

"My poor love," I whisper, cuddling him.

"Well, they did their best," he says, philosophically. I put his socks on for him because he can hardly reach over his own tummy.

Ten days later, Jim is admitted to hospital for the day. They begin with X rays and a scan before draining six litres of fluid from his stomach through a drip attached to his abdomen.

I spend the morning circling the magazine stand downstairs and haunting the coffee hall, waiting and writing. I begin to memorise the entire layout of the hospital, as the endless stream of altered people pass back and forth before me, some on crutches, some on stretchers, some on autopilot. Doctors hold snatched conferences on the concourse and nurses bustle past, fresh from training. Hospital porters amble by and cleaners take up their mops. In a scene reminiscent of the musical, Oliver, I expect them to break out in song because it looks so carefully orchestrated.

At 5 p.m. Jim is ready for collection. He weighs a stone and a half less than he did at the beginning of the day. His trousers nearly fall down until he tightens his belt around them.

"At least I can put my own socks on at last!" He smiles, tying his laces up and grabbing his coat.

"Goodbye, Handsome James!" A passing nurse beams, waving to him.

Jim grins at me.

"Yeah, about that. Don't let it go to your head!" I hiss, booting him up the backside as he winks at her.

Jim can breathe easy at last. He flings his wedding ring absent-mindedly at the checkout girl in Waitrose as we queue to pack our shopping. It is not intentional. Since the ascitic drain, his hands are no longer swollen. His wedding ring is suddenly several sizes too big for him, but he insists on wearing it anyway.

"Are you making a pass at me?" She grins, picking it up and handing it back to him.

"Hey, you! You don't get out of our marriage that easily!" I grin.

"Maybe we should get it adjusted though?" I venture, swirling it around his outstretched finger.

"No point," he replies. "I'm never sure what size I'm going to be next." He pauses. "I'm like the Incredible Shrinking Man. That's my Super Hero power – shrinking down at a moment's notice!"

Later, I eye the trail of abandoned socks lying next to the laundry basket at home and call to him, wondering if the ability to vanish at will hasn't just been added to his list of super powers.

CHAPTER 53

Jim is as pale as a Joshua Reynolds portrait and freezing cold to the touch, even though the sun is gently warming our backs as we walk towards the Thames. I want to believe him when he says it is just a touch of flu, but his complexion is translucent and bloodless.

I hold his hand, gently, as if he were my child, in need of tender care and protection. We wend our way through the Saturday streets towards the Tate Modern Exhibition.

Edward Hopper is a recent discovery for me. Nighthawks is brilliantly displayed in the gallery, far superior in its original form, to any slavish reproduction. Jim stands transfixed in front of it, drinking in every detail, while the painted figures on the canvas remain hunched over the bar, each lost in their own private thoughts. Hopper achieved his first exhibition courtesy of his wife Jo, a talented artist in her own right.

"See, it's true what they say," I grin. "Behind every great man is a great woman!"

Jim shoots around, feigning surprise at finding me behind him.

"What's your point?" He laughs.

"Oh, you'll keep!" I mutter under my breath and he grins, hugging me to him.

Hopper's art is simplicity itself and therein lies his elegance. His sitters are watchful, gazing out at New England landscapes and water fronts.

Sun in an Empty Room is particularly poignant. Four walls, sunlit with no figures at all. It speaks only of the void of afterwards and I feel deeply moved by its honesty. Two Comedians depicts Hopper and his wife, painted lovingly as pantomime actors taking their final bow on stage. It is the last scene of the exhibition. I take a deep breath and start at the beginning again with Yawl Riding a Swell. I need the freedom of its buoyant sea breeze to calm this tightening in my heart.

Back at home, we are biding our time, bobbing up and down on the surface of life like boats on the ocean, ever mindful of the oncoming squall.

Jim slips effortlessly back into his favourite role, acting the part of a man who has nothing to worry about, with me cast as his overwrought wife. He even succeeds in convincing me that we can book a holiday abroad, in Barcelona.

"The doctors think it's a good idea, for us both to have a bit of a break," he assures me.

I remain unconvinced, anxious about the implications of being abroad with him so ill. His health has been far more precarious of late.

"You worry too much," he breezes.

"Someone has to," I counter.

He distracts me by juggling three satsumas from the fruit bowl in that ridiculous fashion of his. Unable to help laughing, I snatch them from him one by one and replace them in the bowl, forcing him to sober up and face reality.

"Seriously," he says, gazing into my eyes. "It'll be fine. We'll just have a nice time away from it all."

That's all we can hope for, a break from reality; we know it will catch up with us soon enough.

Dreaming of Gaudi, I sleep beneath the secluded archways of the Sagrada Familia, watching the building melt and drip towards me, like molten candle wax. I wake at the three in the morning, haunted, soaked in perspiration, and reach across to him.

"You OK?" Jim murmurs, clutching me to him.

"It was just a dream," I reply, but I am chilled to the marrow all the same.

The next morning, bathed in sunlight, I feel less afraid. Perhaps after all, I am simply being over cautious. I make Jim an early lunch and take it through to him in the lounge.

"Not broccoli again?" He moans, eyeing his plate.

"It'll do you good. We've got to look after you." I scold him..

He pokes his tongue out at me like a recalcitrant child and wrestles me for the TV remote control.

"Just for that I'm going to make you watch Eddie Izzard," he announces.

"See if I care." I kick my slippers off and curl up on the settee beside him with my plate on my lap.

I lose myself momentarily in my book, but I cannot concentrate properly. The words spill out in all directions from the page, incomprehensible to my distracted mind. I am nervous about the prospect of going on holiday, but I cannot tell him that when he is so clearly looking forward to it.

I take myself off for a walk by the sea. Even here, he is at the forefront of my mind. I see the places where we first walked, years before, when everything was new and fresh on the horizon. What if we had known then, what lay ahead? Would it have made any difference at all to us?

I see him, then, striding towards me. It occurs to me, not for the first time, that I must grasp hold of these precious moments and commit them to memory.

"Hello, you! I've missed you!" He smiles, hugging me to him.

"Me too," I grin. "Want an ice cream?"

The holiday, you see, has to start here. There is no other way. There never was.

Chapter 54

"I think I need an ambulance!"

Jim's voice is matter of fact. His request is as absurd as it is shocking.

I am making macaroni cheese in the kitchen. I want to finish grating the cheese, but I come to my senses instead and race down the hall.

"Are you all right?"

Ridiculous question. Jim is hanging over the toilet bowl in the bathroom, on the verge of collapse. Blood is everywhere. On the tiled walls, soaking the carpet, sprayed up against the sink. It is a horror movie, but the camera is still rolling.

"Hold on... I've got my mobile."

Fingers shaking, I dial 999. Thank God they answer swiftly.

"Hello? Yes, my husband is ill. He has hepatitis C." I begin politely, trying desperately to maintain a semblance of normality because all that surrounds me is sheer terror.

"Ambulance!" Jim cries out.

"Ambulance, please." I am remarkably calm now. I do not shout back.

The man on the phone is extremely helpful.

"We've got a paramedic on their way to you now. Stay on the phone. An ambulance is following directly."

Jim is crouched down on the side of the bath now, grabbing tissues and holding them to his mouth. I grasp his shoulder, desperate to steady him.

"It's OK, love, I'm with you. I'm not going to let anything happen.

You're safe."

He looks up at me, then his eyes glaze over, as if he is about to pass out. The man on the phone is still talking me through what to do.

Jim lurches forward and another spray of blood hits the deck. Brighter this time. This is really ominous. He is busy trying to convince me that he is not about to faint.

I slam the toilet lid down, but I don't flush it. It may be crucial to the medics in establishing the stage of gastrointestinal bleed. I am truly horrified by what is happening. I gather his medicines, moving at the speed of light. Grabbing my bag and keys, I remember to check the oven is off. Somewhere in this process, I have opened the front door and collected Jim's shoes and coat. The kitchen floor is covered in dried macaroni, the bathroom is covered in blood. What kind of housewife am I?

The paramedic has arrived and she is fitting an oxygen mask to Jim. Kneeling beside him, she reassures him, and I hold his hand.

Can he make it downstairs? The ambulance is on its way but the driver cannot find us through the maze of flats. I go downstairs in search of him. He looks wildly irritated and I find myself apologising to him. Jim has stopped throwing up blood. What if I am wrong? Perhaps it was something he'd eaten at lunch time? Am I no better than those time-wasters you hear about so often on TV? Old ladies who call up the emergency services because they can't get Channel 5 on their free-view sets?

In the back of the ambulance, I squeeze Jim's hand. He is deathly pale.

"I'm so sorry," he begins, shaking as he gazes at me.

"I should think so too," I smile, desperate to make things better for him. "I'd only cleaned that bathroom this morning."

Shock has sent us both into lock-down. I am operating like an automaton. Only later do I realise what Jim has already grasped. He is dying.

The ambulance men stretcher Jim into the Medical Assessment Unit. He is transferred onto a trolley bed to await the doctor.

In exactly two hours time, my father will arrive at our flat for his dinner. He will let himself in using the spare key and will see blood splattered up the bathroom wall and think there has been a murder. If I leave Jim's side, even for a second, I risk not being there if he has another haemorrhage. I take a calculated risk and dive out into the corridor.

"Dad! I can't stop right now, but I can't make your tea tonight. Jim's good, but I forgot he had a check up today. No, nothing major, honestly. Just routine. We're at QA. Talk later. Sorry."

I snap my mobile off and race back to Jim's side. I reel off a list of his medications to the young male nurse who is attending to him. Jim's body contorts then rears up, like a lion, and a huge red arc of blood emerges from his mouth. All hell breaks loose. Shouting, a rush of beds on wheels, a tangle of handbags, coats and shoes and we find ourselves in the emergency room, in the presence of fifteen doctors and nurses. I have no idea how we got here. Then as quickly as they came, they vanish. All of them. We are left alone, Jim and I, only curtains separating us from the outside ward. Blood is erupting from Jim in volcanic proportions.

"Please! Somebody help us!" I yell. Why have they all left? This is unbelievable. I grab a Kenwood mixing bowl I brought from home, in case he was ill in the ambulance. Balancing it under his chin, I do my best to prop Jim's head forward. It is full to the brim with blood in mere seconds. In they charge! The cavalry is back! A doctor tilts Jim's head to the left and blood streams from his mouth down the side of the sheets. His face is grey, unrecognisable. I am clutching the blood-filled bowl to me, shaking uncontrollably. Everyone is shouting orders. A nurse grabs my arm and swiftly removes me from the scene, taking the bowl from me.

"Come on, let's get you out of here, shall we?"

I am sat here now, in the silence of the waiting room, listening to the clamour of hell in my head.

I have never been religious, then or since, but I have always had a keen sense of God. If I stay quietly in the room, with the hospital magazine balanced on my knee and the old telephone handset parked beside me, then somehow I can pretend to contain the horror of what is happening beyond these four walls.

Hours later, someone arrives to speak to me.

"We can't tell you anything at all yet, I'm afraid. It may be hours until we can."

I nod, grateful for this news of nothing. It is bad, I know that, of course. Do I want to ring anyone? I can't think straight. We only lost Mum recently in this very hospital. It doesn't seem fair to call my family. I can manage, just. If I sit and do nothing. I can't think who to ring. There are friends who would come but nobody but me knows the true nature of Jim's illness or his past heroin addiction. I am stuck. I want to keep him safe. I can't begin to explain to people. Not right now.

How would they all react, if they knew? Would they really understand? Would they see him for the good man that he is? Would my father see finally that not all heroin addicts are irredeemably bad? Some hold down decent jobs, once they are clean.

Eventually, wearying of all other avenues of retreat, I pick up the Gideon Bible left abandoned on the table. My eyes alight immediately on Matthew 6:34. Sufficient unto the day is the evil thereof.

CHAPTER 55

I am sitting in the Intensive Care Unit waiting room, praying for a miracle. Jim is lying in bed, the other side of the wall, waiting to die.

"I'm terribly sorry, we have done all we can, but he has lost so much blood." The doctor is crying as she sits talking to me. "He was so brave. He was barely conscious when we did the final endoscopy. We weren't able to sedate him, because of the blood loss, but he gave me consent to go ahead anyway." She pauses, composing herself. "We're not expecting him to make it through the night. I'm so sorry to have to break this to you."

I nod, barely able to comprehend what she is really saying to me.

"Thank you for telling me," I whisper.

"Would you like us to call someone for you?"

I shake my head, then pause,

"His sister is in Glasgow," I begin. "I should ring her."

The doctor nods gently.

I stare bleakly at the painting on the wall. Edward Hopper's Yawl Riding a Swell. Strange to think that only recently Jim and I were wandering around an exhibition of his work at Tate Modern.

"God," I whisper under my breath. "I can't do anything to save him now, but you can. Only you can decide what happens next."

It is a quiet act of surrender. I am beyond pleading, beyond begging. It is the first of the miracles. I sit wrapped in a blanket, waiting in the dead of night. My father appears with sandwiches and a flask and we sit together in the sauna-like heat of the windowless room waiting, until at last I make him go home to sleep.

A gentle knock at the door brings me back to the present.

"We wondered if you would like to come and sit beside Jim's bed? It might help to comfort him, now that we have cleaned him up a little. But I must warn you, there is a lot of blood."

I am already up and following the nurse in.

Here he is, my lovely man. Fastened to the bed, like Aslan the lion, defeated by the magic from the dawn of time. The curse of death is upon him. The demons have had their day, dancing around him, taunting him and spitting their curse over his life. Now they have left him, believing him dead.

He is grey. All but a corpse lying on his sheets. A vast ventilator tube funnels out of his open mouth, tied on crudely with string, because his tongue is swollen to three times its normal size and is jammed obscenely at the entrance of his mouth. His hand pokes absent-mindedly from the bed, jutting towards my side. I take it gently in my own. His finger nails are outlined in blood, every crevice of his skin, every line on his palm etched red brown like henna. When the veins in his stomach and oesophagus broke open without warning, the blood erupted from him with volcanic force. Thank God the doctor had warned him it might happen and Jim had thought to tell me. You don't know the horrors the human body is capable of until you witness one of them first hand.

Jim is in a coma. All around us, computer screens bank up, monitoring his progress. Oxygen levels, blood pressure, heart rate. He is freezing cold. An inflatable blanket covers him, normally reserved for car crash victims to keep them warm after shock sets in. Jim's temperature is rapidly deteriorating. They do not think he is going to pull through.

I am not permitted to stay beside him.

"You must go home now and get some sleep."

They are serious. They will not even let me sit in the waiting room. I nod silently but am desperate not to leave his side. I have no choice.

They will not permit me to stay.

"We promise we'll ring you the second there is any change in his condition. You can come up as early as you like in the morning. But we have to look after you too, and you must sleep."

It is 2 a.m. Somehow I get back to our flat. I pull the carpet up in the bathroom and, with a Stanley knife, cut the offending pieces into strips and dispose of it. Then I bleach the bathroom from top to bottom and retire to bed, exhausted.

Two and a half hours later, at 4.30, the phone rings.

"Mrs. McPhail? It's Sandra from the hospital. I'm so sorry to disturb you. Jim's results are declining slightly. I thought you would want to know."

I ring for a taxi. Outside it is eerily calm and dark. The taxi driver is kind and unobtrusive. He knows why people go to hospital at this time of the morning.

I am ushered in to Jim's bedside. The night duty nurse gives me a tight, sweet smile.

We wait. I sit on a high stool, holding Jim's limp grey hand. Does he even know that I am here? He is barely registering any signs of life. I watch the meaningless numbers on the monitor rise and fall. I try to push the numbers upwards by sheer effort of will, mindful that now even telepathy may count for something.

Slowly, defying logic, the counts do rise.

Ward round begins promptly, 7 a.m. sharp.

"Where is the GI bleed from last night?" A rather pompous consultant sweeps in, brushing the shoulder of his suit.

The nursing sister descends on him at once. "If, by 'GI bleed' you are referring to Mr. James McPhail, Sir, then the gentleman in question is in this bed and this is his wife."

Suitably chagrined, the consultant has the decency to flush. I am cheering Sister Kathryn on for all I am worth.

The plan is to transfer Jim to Southampton Hospital for an

emergency procedure, to put a stent in his liver, enabling blood flow to bypass it. It might save his life, if he makes it there alive and on time. Otherwise, I will be a widow by tomorrow.

It is an agonising wait. Fifteen hours later, 10 o'clock at night, Jim is miraculously still alive. They finally rush him by ambulance into the night and to the place where the surgeons are waiting.

The operation is declared a resounding success. Jim, however, remains resolutely in a coma. Time has no meaning. Days and nights meld into one. Under the artificial lighting of the Southampton General Intensive Care Unit, it is forever day. Normal life has been suspended. I haven't been to work for two weeks. Instead I perch on a high stool beside Jim's bed, watching and waiting, observing the staff at close quarters. I might as well make myself useful. I think I could probably manage to insert a feeding tube now. Certainly I know how to take blood pressure readings. Instead, I squeeze Jim's hand and concentrate on loving him to my very limits, willing him to survive. Best I stick to my own specialist area. There are experts in all the other fields.

"We need to take him off the ventilator, to see if he can breathe without it," his nurse informs me.

I nod. "Do you think he'll be OK?" I ask, assuming optimism to be the order of the day now the worst is clearly over.

She casts me a curious look in response, as if weighing up what to tell me. She tentatively removes the breathing tube. Jim's chest remains static.

"Come on, love, do it for me, please!" I urge him.

Nothing.

Reluctantly and swiftly, the nurse replaces it.

I do not know what is going on here. Is my husband only artificially alive? Did they lie to me when they told me that he had a chance of survival? I am no expert, but I do know that independent breathing is a prerequisite for continuing to live.

"Is there anything else I can do to help him?" I ask.

She shakes her head. "Has anyone explained to you how serious this really is?" She asks, cautiously. "That there is every likelihood that at some point Jim will experience another gastrointestinal bleed. If he does, he won't survive it a second time."

My heart plummets like a broken lift shaft. I wait in agony now, every shred of hope torn from me. Even if Jim does wake up again, he cannot hope to survive long term. The nurse has said as much. I pour out the story to his consultant, the moment he arrives.

"That's not strictly true," he says, carefully. "There are certain precautions we can take. The main thing we need to do is to ensure that Jim's stent implant doesn't become blocked over time. We have a procedure called a venogram, whereby we can inject a dye into his veins to trace the progress of his blood around his body using a screen. And we can continue to do ultrasound scans too, to keep an eye on him."

I breathe out at last, so grateful to him.

Suddenly Jim is stirring. I take his hand. He is blurry eyed, but nods at me.

"Hello, you! I love you so much! I'm so glad to see you again!" I cannot conceal my excitement.

He squeezes my hand as if to reassure me. He looks like an astronaut who has just touched down to earth from a long space mission.

Dr Rosenberg gives him a welcoming smile. "Hello James! It's very good to see you awake at last. You gave us all quite a shock this time, didn't you?" He is kindness itself, perched on the end of the bed, talking to him. But then a cloud of fellow consultants arrive and he is swiftly absorbed into their number and is gone.

The ventilator is off. The gloves are off. The contest is between Jim and his fellow patient in the next bed. Any minute now, the bell will ring and it will be seconds out. Round two. Into the ring step their appointed nurses. A spare bed is needed urgently here in Intensive Care, which means someone has to go. No one is really well enough to leave for the main medical ward yet, but that is beside the point when space is at a premium. My money is firmly on the blonde female patient. She is sitting upright and hasn't stopped complaining since she arrived. I reckon anyone displaying that much fight is up to battling it out on the main ward, tackling MRSA and Norovirus head on. Both are on special offer this week, courtesy of the NHS in a special two for one deal.

Not my Jim, I think, guarding him fiercely. He is wired up still. Tubes everywhere. It's a much tougher proposition to dismantle Jim from his equipment than it is to move the blonde woman. If I sit on his bed in silent protest, they might reckon without shifting him.

Straws are drawn and everyone holds their breath. Except Jim of course. He is busily making the most of his oxygen tubes. Independent breathing is a bit of a novelty to him still. It's easy to take it for granted unless you're out of the habit. He is keen to get a bit of practice in.

Close to midnight the decision is made to move Jim after all. They bundle his bed out of the ward, tubes tapping the side of his metal bed, as they wheel him on rollers. I grab my handbag and coat and wrestle his shoes free of the bedside cabinet, along with his watch. They don't have time for niceties. The staff here are in the business of saving lives. Every second counts. The next patient is already on his way to them.

Enclosed by curtains, on the General Medical Ward, Jim cannot move, cannot sit up, remains desperately ill. Tears catch in the back of my throat. I have been awake for 36 hours now. I should have started training as a junior doctor while I had the chance. I might have sailed through the sleep deprivation part of the curriculum. I don't want to leave him when he is so vulnerable here. He is incapable of even pushing the bell to summon help if he needs it. He is exhausted. The nurses insist I leave him now, so that we can both get some sleep. The other patients stir briefly, disturbed by his arrival on the ward.

The team and I abandon Jim until the morning.

Bed pans are in the sluice room to my left, but it has taken me three days to establish this vital knowledge. Every time I have attempted to ask, the nurse in question has had to vanish mid sentence, rushed off her feet with so many patients to attend to.

Tenderly, the nurse and I turn Jim towards me and he clings onto my shoulders in order for his bed sheets to be changed beneath him. We indulge in a little kiss. It is the first time I have held him in over ten days. He is tearful.

"What would I do without you?" He asks, quietly.

"Oh, if it wasn't me sat here, it would be another equally gorgeous woman, I'm sure of it!" I grin. "Besides, you'll never have to be without me. Ever."

"Now then, that's quite enough of all that!" Reprimands the nurse, teasing us both. "Any excuse with you two, isn't it?"

We laugh a little, gazing into each other's eyes. I am cut to the quick by the intensity of our love.

"Mr. McPhail is now incontinent, it would appear!" This harsh announcement is delivered loudly by a short-tempered Korean nursing sister who clearly thinks she owns the place. Frankly, I don't care if she does, but she will not treat my husband this way. Jim looks downcast and embarrassed.

"My husband is not incontinent. He manages perfectly well if he is supported. He is simply unable to move unaided, that is all."

She draws up short, but says nothing. Clearly she is not used to being challenged. The health care assistants are privately enjoying her discomfort. Sister moves on. She has softer targets than me to crush. She doesn't need the aggravation.

The rest of the nurses and health care assistants fly around the ward like ministering angels, changing bed sheets, mopping up and administering drugs. They give it their all and then some, twelve hours at a stretch, snatching mere minutes for lunch breaks, late in the afternoon. I don't know how they stand the pace.

Our favourite nurse does all this and then returns home to care for her own elderly mother who lives with her. She is breezily cheery throughout.

"She calls me James," Jim grins. "I like that. It makes me feel special."

In the afternoon, the sister returns to Jim's side and pauses to ask how he is feeling. I smile briefly at her, appreciating our mutual gesture of forgiveness. I have just realised that if I were in her shoes, day in, day out, my professional etiquette might also slip on occasion.

CHAPTER 56

Jim is coming home today and it is my father's seventieth birthday. We have a surprise for him, a hastily decorated cake I bought at Asda in between hospital visits, as well as the news that Jim has contracted MRSA. I hate short-changing my father. Jim is weak and frail. He makes it up the stairs and insists on staying up long enough to watch my father unwrap his presents and have a coffee with us.

My father kisses me on the forehead and I watch him drive away. My heart longs to make it all up to him. He has had a rotten time of it since Mum died.

Jim collapses into bed immediately. He is too exhausted by the journey home to do anything but sleep. I am too ecstatic at the miracle of him lying beside me to do anything other than stay bolt awake. I watch him all night long, unable to believe that he has survived.

In the morning he stirs, dreadfully thirsty and terribly hungry. For nearly fourteen days he has existed on liquids only. Fortified drinks replaced the Ng feeding tube. I set to work. I make crustless toast and cut it into heart shapes, covered in butter and strawberry jam. He beams and reaches to me for a kiss.

I cook a macaroni cheese and get to finish it this time. The flat is full of bare floorboards where I took up the carpets.

Jim is a hungry cuckoo, famished and bed bound in a duvet nest. He eats every meal as if it is his last. I slice tomatoes onto macaroni cheese. I tempt him with marshmallows and rice puddings and soups.

He desperately needs to put on weight. He shivers as I help him into the bath. His ribs stick out of his sides, like a prisoner of war.

I am shocked at how frail he is. He holds on to my shoulders and I help him step out onto the mat afterwards. How must it feel to him, being back in the room where it all took place? Our beautiful white bathroom. Thankfully it is summer, or it would be too cold for these bare floorboards.

The district nurse arrives while I am still wrestling with the tidying up. What must she think of our chaotic household? I am busy reprimanding myself, but she hardly notices. She is a dear lady, cheering Jim up no end.

Perched beside Jim's bed is a little figurine of Buddha that I bought him as a gift. He carries a feather quill in his hand – a writer, just like Jim. Only, Jim is eyeing him uncomfortably.

"What is it?" I ask

"It's just that I asked God to save me, in hospital. I was worried. He might not like it."

I stare at him, amazed. This is not the Jim I know.

"God wouldn't mind a bit! He knows how much I love you, doesn't He? He's not going to mind me giving you a present to cheer you up now, is he?"

I return to busying myself with the dusting, but am puzzled just the same.

CHAPTER 57

Jim is lying in bed, feeling queasy. His eyes reveal his fright that this might herald another gastrointestinal bleed.

"I don't feel very well," he mumbles, reaching for me.

"There, now." I lie beside him, taking his hand in my own.

"I think I'm going to be sick," he begins, anxious not to alarm me, but clearly terrified at the thought of another ordeal.

The district nurse rings the doorbell and I leap up in gratitude at her timing.

She smoothes Jim's forehead with an expert hand and takes his temperature.

"How long have you felt like this, my love?"

"A few minutes," Jim replies.

She nods and turns to me.

"I think you might need to call an ambulance if he continues to feel sick. It's Sunday, so don't bother with the GP first. Dial 999. I hate to say this, but this is the worst possible day for it to happen because the service is always stretched to breaking point at the weekend. You don't want to delay getting him in."

After she leaves, we lie together side by side, hearts pounding. I pray fervently he will be all right. I cannot bear him having to endure the fear of this moment; after all he has been through.

"I'm not going anywhere, I promise. I will not leave your side. I will make sure you are safe, do you hear me."

He nods, listlessly, his eyes wide and alarmed, and squeezes my hand. Moments later, the nausea passes. His relief and mine are palpable.

Everything is condensed to the present moment. Life shrinks in direct proportion to the height of the mountain Jim has to climb. It is three weeks before he is able to get up from bed and pad into the lounge. Another week before he is able to venture step by step outdoors, clinging to my arm for support. He has to wear his slippers because the wounds on his ankle and the swelling of his limbs make it impossible to tolerate his shoes. He struggles valiantly across the road, then sits exhausted on the garden wall opposite. Moments later, he stirs again.

"Don't do more than you are able to. Remember it's your first time out in weeks..."

But Jim, as ever, is determined. He rises up and manages a few more unsteady steps, before sinking down again. He shakes his head, tearful yet triumphant. Up he gets again.

"Please, Jim," I beg. "No more today, eh?"

"I want to prove to myself that I can get to the end of the road," he insists.

"And you will. Just not today. It's too much, too soon."

He gives me a truculent look, then nods in agreement and we shuffle back indoors. When we get there, I discover I too have been wearing my slippers. In all the excitement, I forgot to put my shoes on. We burst out laughing.

*

Outside summer blazes on without us.

Later, I find Jim lying in bed. He has snuck off, not wanting me to know he is upset.

"I shall never be able to take you anywhere nice again!" He says. His face is so sad as he clings to my shoulder.

"Yes, you will!" I insist. "We have plenty of good times ahead of us, just you wait and see."

"Sorry," he says.

Whatever for, I should like to know. He has only ever made me happy.

Within days he has made it up the road to the corner shop and back with only three rest stops en route.

I am up at 6 a.m. I get dressed. I am returning to work at last.

"Are you sure you're going to be OK?" I ask, desperate for reassurance.

"Of course. I can ring you, can't I? If I need to?"

"Oh, love, of course you can. I shall ring you just as soon as I get there. You don't hesitate if you need me at all. I've left your mobile here, right by the bed, all charged up. You just call me whenever you want to, you promise?"

He nods in agreement. He looks sad that I am going. I am guilt-stricken at abandoning him when it is obvious that he still needs me. The doctor on his home visits urged me to remain with him, but what else can we do? I have to earn a living and this situation is long-term. We have no choice.

Back at work, everyone is kind and nobody really understands. They treat Jim's illness as a cross between a bad bout of flu and a case of exaggeration. How can I possibly get across to them the fact he very nearly died? Even when I tell them, it's as if I hit a screen and they still do not take on board the severity of the situation. I am rapidly learning that this is a standard response to the threat of mortality. People are too afraid to acknowledge it, in case it's catching. Bad news, people. We are all, without exception, going to die. At work I can barely concentrate for thinking of him, watching the clock for the moment when I can get away.

He is overjoyed at my return.

"Please be honest, Jim. If you need me, I'll be here for you and work can take a running jump."

He pauses thoughtfully, his dark soulful eyes resting gently on my face.

JAMES WITH A SILENT C

"I was a bit nervous at first, but it's all right now. I know it's going to be all right, isn't it?"

"Of course it is," I assure him, turning the light out as I climb into bed beside him.

Suddenly, it is abundantly clear that we are both grappling around in darkness, pinning our hopes on some unknown future promise. Endeavouring to reassure one another without having any real answer.

Sunlight, like hope, pours gently through the windows each morning. The sun has a way of making you feel cared for when all else fails.

The Festival of the Sea dawns clear and bright. The sea front is awash with tall ships, in full regalia, out in force for the celebration of the 200th Anniversary of the Battle of Trafalgar. The sun blazes a trail of gold across the water.

I am alone, tramping the pavements, admiring the coloured bunting that trails from the Victorian lamp posts of Old Portsmouth. Nelson walks by, posing briefly to enquire of a local about the progress of his fleet. He turns and reveals himself to be a pensioner in fancy dress. I smile and take his photograph.

Everywhere I go, I snap pictures, anxious that Jim, alone at home, should not miss out.

Later that evening, he manages to shuffle round to the corner of the street. We stand watching the Red Arrows fly past in formation. The pilots circle directly overhead and trail a bright red heart in the wake of their jets.

"Ahh! Look, that is for us!" Jim says. Sometimes, it seems the universe knows exactly what you need.

That night, amid the fireworks, tall ships emerge from the shadows of the sea, lit up like ghostly galleons. An entire fleet of sailors raise their caps as one in a silent salute to the past and are gone. Only the moon is left behind.

Time is so precious now. Summer slinks away, leaving behind an empty husk of itself. The evening light suffuses us in a lingering golden glow. We wander round the common and I lean against the old oak tree. Jim takes my photograph, smiling at me long after he has clicked the shutter. Our unspoken thoughts honour the fact that he knows and I know.

Fate has given us an impossible, beautiful, priceless gift and placed it in our hands. We hold the knowledge of our own fragility.

I clown around, peering at him from behind a tree trunk, poking my tongue out at him, urging him to play, lest we sully the moment with sentiment. Our unspoken longing for each other tears at us. His kiss alights gently on the back of my neck as he pulls me to him.

"I love you."

"Me too."

"We're incredibly lucky, you know. Not everyone has this, do they?"

I swing my arms around, enjoying the cool air on my face. The scent of the gone-to-bed flowers fills my senses as they close their petals for the night. Daisies, random as raindrops sprinkle the grass, reminding me of the chains I made so long ago, threaded through the stems of childhood dreams.

We head towards home. Another day has slipped through our fingers, try as we might to hold onto it.

PART 9

CHAPTER 58

Ward C10 Addenbrooke's Hospital Cambridge
Liver Transplant Assessment Unit

"Tell me I'm dreaming," I whisper to Jim.

I am horrified. Everywhere we look, corpselike figures are propped up in beds or wooden armchairs. Their features slowly drip toward the floor, like molten candle wax. With their iodine stained faces, heavily jaundiced, they stare up at us as we walk down the ward. I am reminded of the king's daughter, in an ancient fairy tale, who is commanded to look neither to the right nor to the left as she makes her way down the hallway.

It is as if we have entered a war zone, shortly after ceasefire. Everywhere, bodies lie prostrate on trolley beds, upper arms worn away, muscles wasted, hair plastered thinly over exposed scalps. Why has this atrocity been hushed up? Why does the media not break open this secret?

Shuffling along, with an IVU drip on castors, a man in his late fifties looks up. His stomach is obscenely distended, as if, like a parasite, it has turned on its host and is feasting on his remains. He eyes Jim with a detached, sympathetic smile before retiring to bed.

The nurses are oblivious to our shock. They have seen it all before. Bustling and business-like ahead of us, clipboard under her arm, the ward sister wheels out the pharmaceutical trolley. A cleaning woman quickly pulls her mop away, out of our path. I feel guilty walking over the tiles she has so diligently cleaned, but she smiles as if to say she understands.

Jim is undressed and put into a hospital gown. I fold his clothes neatly and put them into the cupboard beside his bed.

"The doctor will be in to see you both shortly."

"Thank you."

We are alone. Jim has a room to himself. You can see the fields from the window, the rolling Cambridgeshire countryside disappearing into the darkness of a November evening. I sit on the edge of the bed and he pats my knee with his hand.

"You all right?" I ask, smiling.

He nods, arms stretched out by his side, as if he is conducting a brief check, to make sure that all of him is safely installed in situ.

A huge dark head with matted fur nudges open the door. I jump up, alarmed as an enormous black dog on a lead bursts into the room. A woman with wild red hair and spectacles beams at us both. From her ears dangle earrings made out of seashells. I wonder if she hears the ocean in them?

"Hello there! Don't mind us popping in, do you? We're from a charity that brings pets to patients. Would you like to meet the girls?"

The girls, it transpires, are two vast and adorable mongrels. They approach the bed, wanting us to make a fuss of them.

"Oh, they're lovely!" I sigh.

The woman nods, "Yes they are. We take them around the wards. People who've been here a long time get cheered up by them. Lots of them miss their own pets back at home, you see."

As she departs, the dogs bound enthusiastically along behind her.

We look at each other and grin.

"Bit surreal, isn't it?" Jim observes with his usual wry smile.

The doctor taps the door and enters. I get up, so he can sit beside Jim.

"So, welcome Mr. McPhail. Lovely to meet you. You got up here all right?"

Jim nods. He gives a brief history of his illness at the doctor's request.

"Ah yes, I see you had a GI episode in the summer. Quite an alarming one, too, by the looks of things." He eyes Jim's medical records.

The doctor is clarifying the notes he has but he is also testing Jim's own recollection of events as part of his assessment. Jim draws a blank suddenly, confused as to dates. He looks briefly embarrassed.

"What year did I start interferon?" He searches my face for clues. I am his back-up. His infallible memory bank.

"It's OK, Jim. You're just tired, I expect," the doctor reassures him.

I know perfectly well that for Jim, the most frightening aspect of his illness is the possibility of becoming mentally less alert and sharp. He would hate that.

We are given a brief outline of the week's programme of tests.

"I'd like you to begin with twenty-four hours urinary collection." The doctor hands Jim a cardboard bottle and beams in apology. "Nice to meet you both. The transplant co-ordinator will be in next."

They are practised and professional, putting you at ease by informing you of every stage of treatment. It always helps to know in advance what to expect next. Of course the final outcome is one that nobody can predict. Did we but know it, we are in a rare state of grace.

I wake up the next morning in the house set in the hospital grounds where I am staying to be close to Jim. Trying to make the best of things, I catch the bus into town, as I am not permitted to visit him until 2 p.m. Cambridge is beautiful, even in late November. I wander over a little halfpenny bridge and see ducks paddling along the river's edge, squabbling among themselves in easy domesticity. Punts are bobbing on the water, tethered, going nowhere until summer calls them out next year. I discover an old church, set high on a grassy hill, and wander through its grounds.

Cyclists hurl over the bridge, their wheels like runaway hoops.

I lean against a lamp post to shield myself from them. Surrounded by such beautiful architecture and solemn traditions, I dream of a lost academic career and the sacred ancient walls reinforce my melancholic mood.

I wish Jim was here with me right now. He would love it too, this university town. But he is in a hospital today. The students have their timetables to adhere to and so does Jim. Lung function test today. Let's hope he passes with flying colours.

I drink a coffee in Heffers bookshop, feeling ridiculously lonely. I examine postcards of St John's College and feel the urge to send one home, though we are not on holiday. I envy the students passing by with their rosy, assured futures.

At 2 o'clock I return to the ward, steeling myself for the walk past the beds of drowning faces. My man is the exception that will prove the rule. He is a survivor.

"Hello, you!" He beams as I enter.

"How are you?" I begin.

"I've missed you!" He confides. "Did you have a nice morning?"

"It's beautiful, Cambridge," I assure him. "I've got lots of photos to show you. But what's been happening to you, first?"

He lifts his cardboard bottle and eyes it ruefully. "Got to do another twenty-four hours worth," he says. "I've had to drink tons of water. I was up and down all night long."

Stoic man.

"Never mind," I rub his knee. "How are you feeling?"

"OK. I really slept a lot. I said to them, I ought to be getting up now, but they seem to think I should rest in bed while I have the chance."

I nod in agreement. "Do you good. Have you had any lunch?"

"Not yet." He peers into my bag as if I might have something for him. "Have you bought me a present?"

I pull out a bookmark shaped like a monkey and an Irvine Welsh book.

"Ah!" He is pleased with them. He places them together on his bed.

"This city is mad for cyclists!" I suddenly remember, thinking of them whizzing by me. "Honestly you would not believe how long it takes to cross a road here."

Jim hushes his voice to a whisper, distracted suddenly. He rests his hands on the top of his sheets, like a neighbour leaning over a garden fence, full of gossip.

"I think the man next door to me is an alcoholic," he confides.

"Oh, yes?"

"He had a GI bleed in the night."

"Oh, no! Are you sure? I thought I saw him leaning out of the window, smoking, just as I came by."

Jim nods, primly, turning down his sheet.

"He's not meant to. The nurses were telling him off for it."

Curiosity impels me to glance in at the man on my way out of the ward. He is lying in bed, eyes open, gazing heavenward. What do you do when you are on death row? The only answer it seems is to cling to your creature comforts, even if they are going to cost you the very life you are longing to preserve. Fear is a huge factor in blind stupidity. Many of the people in here run foul of alcohol or drugs because they do not feel worthy of love in the first place, perhaps because of past events in their lives. Their very behaviour is driven by guilt and shame. So when you try to convince them that they deserve a second chance in life, courtesy of another's untimely death, every ounce of guilt comes to the surface. So they give nature a helping hand in finishing the job rather than giving themselves a second chance. They don't deserve it, do they? I see the man again, later that week, hanging on to an IVU drip, like a commuter aboard a rush hour train. Boldly setting out, fag in hand, he is heading for that undiscovered Marlboro country from which no traveller returns. He disappears through a door marked Exit and stands on the landing, smoking. I wonder how long it will be for him?

Ward C10 is mainly for patient assessments. To get on to the liver transplant list, you need a referral from your consultant hepatologist. They consider the facts of your case and look at the balance of probabilities. This is a polite medical term for whether you are likely to be alive or not in six months time.

My man is sleeping now. When the person you love more than anyone else in the world is declared terminally ill, you face two choices. You can walk away, abandon ship and pretend you never truly loved him in the first place. Or you can climb right into the boat with him, knowing that at some point, you are both going to be dashed to pieces on the rocks and that only one of you will survive.

For me, the choice was made the moment I set eyes on him. After that, there was never any question of going back.

CHAPTER 59

Back from Cambridge, the chasm between ordinary life and the looming transplant is widening.

We are relieved to discover that nothing has really changed in our absence. I unpack the suitcase while Jim runs a bath. We settle down to watch Larry Sanders. He picks up a hooker just so that he has a passenger in his car and can legally use the fast lane on the freeway. Larry, that is, not Jim. I don't stand for that sort of thing. Larry has a long suffering wife. I don't know how she puts up with him.

I snuggle down in bed beside Jim, glad to be home. Nothing has touched us this time. I close my eyes, willing sleep to come, to obliterate my fears for a few precious hours.

People think it is easier to deal with the gradual decline of someone you love, rather than experiencing the short sharp shock of sudden death. But terminal illness does not follow any text book in its progression. There are peaks of recovery and troughs of depression that are impossible to predict. In truth, there is no easy way to come to terms with terminal disease. It is a battle all the way, both for patient and for carer.

Our roles as husband and wife are rapidly recast. I help him to bath. He recovers. Slowly he regains his strength and our roles revert again. He persuades me not to fuss. He is fine.

He is desperate for a cigarette, yet he never complains. The brutality of his close brush with death convinced him of the folly of smoking or drinking. I admire him for that; it is not as if anyone is offering him a cast iron guarantee. Give up smoking and you will live.

Never let a drop of alcohol touch your lips and you will live.

Jim has finally beaten all his addictions. Except he can't stop taking pictures. Every time I turn around, the camera is pointing in my direction. The writers in our arts centre group are ceremoniously lined up outside their new meeting place and snapped in honour of his visit. He captures the evening sun dappling the trees, the beautiful verdigris-wrought gates of the university, a little starling sitting on a wall. He doesn't want to miss a second of it. He captures it all, storing the camera in his jacket pocket, close to his heart. The everyday is breathtakingly extraordinary.

Why do we only choose to truly open our eyes towards the end? To savour the sweet sad truth that there isn't a forever?

I cannot turn the pages anymore. I am afraid to look beyond this one, for fear of finding out what will become of us. Time, though, continues ever on.

Jim becomes the child I never had and my inherent need to nurture is strangely satisfied by looking after my big man. He lies in bed, waiting to be fed. On Sundays, I stand in the kitchen, baking trays of shortbread. He sleeps most of the time. Every now and then I tiptoe down the hall to steal a glance at him. Sometimes he is dreaming. Today, he is softly crying to himself.

"I'm so sorry," he pulls me to him. What for, I don't know. He only ever made me happy.

"Let it all out," I insist. I have learned at least, that it is best to cry. I no longer tell him not to. He clings to me as if I might somehow still save him. He knows that I will never give up trying.

Finally, we decide to challenge time, to take on our adversary. It may be our last chance. We decide to go back to Canterbury, to see if it is as we remember it.

It is winter. The streets are alive with their own fairy tale. The Big Issue seller on the corner is surely a long lost prince, disguised as a beggar.

"Come on, mate, please buy it! I'm freezing my balls off here and it's my last copy."

He is very convincing, this prince; a method actor, he has it down to a fine art. He jerks his head towards us, his spiky ginger hair topped with snowflakes, a shivering grey dog on a rope at his side.

Jim presses two pound coins into his hand and shakes his head at the offer of the magazine. "Keep it, mate, you can sell it on."

I turn the corner and squeeze his hand.

"That was nice of you."

Jim grins. "He's probably pulling a fast one, but you know, I'd rather be a fool than wrong."

"That's exactly why I love you – fool!" I grin, kissing him and wrapping myself tightly around him.

The world has turned to ice. The Snow Queen of long ago has it in her grasp. Everywhere the snowflakes fall like tiny shards, concealing the truth.

The cathedral is majestic in the dark. Rushing back to our lodgings, we too are pilgrims, treading a path of love. History surrounds us with its ancient oak beams and its lantern-lit streets, but the people who once mattered here are gone.

Indoors, we warm ourselves by drinking hot chocolate and eating toasted tea cakes. Everything is precious now. We lie in bed in the morning watching the snow fall over the eaves of the house opposite, listening to the boxwood flute of a morning blackbird and the swishing of car tyres on the road outside.

I am already grieving. I have lost the certainty of always having him near me. I bury my head in a book, Brighton Rock. The unrequited love that the girl feels for Pinky upsets me. Jim is holding me as I weep. He doesn't mind that it is over a made-up story.

But then nothing is real anymore. Only love. What are we to one another but a constant reminder of what we cannot have? We are not, after all, composed of shoes or jobs or coats or films or books, all of which will now outlive us.

It is silent here. Just us. Time has slowed down to indulge our need for one another. I do not think ahead. I dare not think what this moment will cost us one day, him and me.

All of us cling to the illusion of immortality, deceiving ourselves that we will be the exceptions in escaping the end. We remain in denial about our physical forms one day failing us until, faced with the devastating affect of illness, we are finally forced to grasp the truth. Death nearly always comes as a shock and a surprise. Even when we know it is inevitable. None of us have a frame of reference for the annihilation of everything we are and have been. We are all children, lost in a hall of mirrors, our distorted images appearing real. We are phantasmagoria on whom the light shines but briefly. God, it seems, will not be reasoned with. It is only in the depths of true grief that one truly experiences His presence. Only in the place of greatest suffering that He awaits us, arms outstretched.

We wander around St Augustine's Abbey in the snow. Ducks queue up beside the frozen water, waiting for a turn on the ice. We are the only visitors here today and the friendly receptionist is delighted to see us. It is impossibly peaceful in the grounds. You could be forgiven for thinking all is well for us. I hold his gloved hand in my own and our breath streams white in front of us. How many whispered prayers rose up from this ground in time past?

Back in the streets, we while away the hours in a rabbit warren of antique shops. Animal walking canes, gentlemen's hat stands, cigarette cases and silver brooches. Books line the walls of our favourite shop, but even they cannot save us now. Lost in translation, all the poems are achingly sad. The city walls rise up strongly in ancient stone, but even they must yield eventually to time which flows beneath the ice, beyond the river, undeterred by anyone.

CHAPTER 60

The train rounds the corner towards the coast, and there it is, just like it was all those years before when I was a child. Devon, with its sparkling sapphire sea, calling us to it.

Jim sits opposite me and we gaze adoringly at each other. We have never quite recovered from the miracle of our continued existence after we so nearly lost one another last year.

His health, of course, is gradually failing. Let us not dishonour each other by pretending otherwise. Our love may be forever, but our physical selves must perish one day. Let me look at him while I can, even though it brings sorrow. It is the undercurrent that drives the tide, after all.

The soil is red here and the cliff tops rise splendidly from the sea. We pass through Dawlish, with its toy town bridge, its ducks and its quaint shop fronts, and on towards Torquay.

The taxi from the station climbs the hills after driving along the shimmering bay. I squeeze Jim's knee, unable to contain my excitement at being here at last.

His already brown arms reach for our cases from the boot of the car and we wend our way up the steep driveway to the guest house.

He looks resplendent in cornflower blue shirt and jeans and casual summer shoes. I want to capture this moment with him, and every other moment, and hold them forever in a jar, but like those butterflies of long ago, each of these precious snapshots is fleeting. Beautiful, ephemeral, and vanishing all too swiftly.

At night, baby owls play on the rooftops. The wide sweep of the bay is lit by the full July moon which shines its blazing torch on the boats in the harbour, bobbing like cotton reels on the waves. There are a hundred darting firefly lights in the houses around us. I sit in the magic of the early hours, on the window ledge of the bay window. Out there in the dark, foxes and badgers forage in the woods at the back of the house and a barn owl sweeps by like a silent winged ghost.

"Come back to bed," you call me.

We lie there, afterwards, in a tangle of limbs, barely knowing where one begins and the other ends. Flushed and exhilarated, hearts pounding with our wild love. A rare peace descends. We are in harmony with everything that surrounds us. We become absorbed into our surroundings, part of the tree branches which nod in the night as a kestrel flies from them. We are the moths that dance in the street lamps, like dusky shadows. We are the silver platter of the moon on which the night mysteriously dines. We are the secrets of the sea, the comings and goings of the tide as our beginnings and endings overlap and come full circle in endless narrative. We are conjoined twins, poets and visionaries. Two souls linked forever.

We may be all of these magical things but we are rubbish at sharing the bedclothes. Now that it is too hot for a duvet, we wrestle over the single sheet that covers our bodies. I give up and wander through to the spare room and climb into the single bed, but moments later I am imagining burglars and seeing witch shadows, so back I go, quaking, to be beside you. I could never sleep alone now.

You laugh and call me a cowardly custard, but you hold me, just the same.

Next morning we are up and filling our lungs with good sea air. I stagger down to the beach in my high heels, complaining about my self imposed discomfort. You tolerate me and ignore my grouching. I take your photograph as you lean against the rock formation but I also capture your image on my heart, recording it forever. Every moment. Nothing missed.

How careless we were, before we knew. I can hardly remember what it was like in those heady first days when I thought we would be together for ever. Now time has let out its cruel measuring tape only so far. At some point, it will be reeled back in.

But we have now. We have a rare beautiful freedom of a Monday morning on a beach. How I long to have given you an entire lifetime of such moments. How very much you deserve them. Instead I offer you just one. Let us spend it carefully, for spend it we must. So mindful are we of its transience, that in the end we spend it carelessly. To cling on now would cause us more pain.

We hurl our cards in the air and let them fall. Life is the dealer and this is the hand we were dealt with from the start.

CHAPTER 61

In common with London taxi drivers, the porters at Addenbrooke's Hospital have to do the knowledge on starting employment there. They are issued with a map covering several miles of hospital wards. With over six thousand medical personnel and thousands of patients, the hospital occupies a vast tract of land. I frequently get lost on my way to see Jim and today is no exception.

A porter speeds past me and swiftly puts me on the right track. I half expect Gatso cameras to be set up in the corridors so that the government don't miss the chance to swoop down on any speeding offences and make a quick buck in the process.

Jim is awaiting a final assessment for the transplant list. He sits patiently in a wheelchair as the porters and I wheel him down to the X Ray Department.

Recently, his illness has taken more of a toll. His upper arms are emaciated and he is gaunt. The hollows of his cheekbones are more pronounced and his eyes have dark shadows under them. He is so thin he has been put on a protein-rich diet. He holds my hand as we roll along the corridor and the two porters, only young lads, laugh and joke with each other at our side.

Later, a doctor comes to examine him, running his hands over his spleen and liver and asking him to raise his right hand in the air to check for tremors.

"Do you suffer any confusion at all, Jim?"

Jim shakes his head firmly. My heart drops.

"Jim..." I urge gently.

The doctor turns sharply to look at me.

"Have you noticed any changes in his behaviour recently?"

Jim is glowering, daring me to speak out.

"I have," I admit reluctantly. The last thing I want to do is betray Jim's confidence, but this charade has gone on long enough.

"I'm sorry, love, but you know I've said to you in shops... when you're counting out change at the till, it's..." I wrestle with my conscience, but the doctor waits patiently and urges me on. "He's usually so sharp but now it takes him ages, as if he can't quite work out what's going on sometimes."

The doctor nods. "That is important. It could be an indicator of encephalopathy."

This condition is caused by an accumulation of toxins in the bloodstream which normally the liver would remove. Encephalopathy causes confusion, irritation and in severe cases leads to coma. I have been warned several times what to watch out for. Jim though, is having none of it.

"Why did you tell him that about me? It's a lie!" He is bitterly upset with me.

I sit beside his bed on the ward, trying to pacify him.

"Because I love you, and I'm not going to lie for you. Not when it's not in your best interests. You need that transplant, Jim, and all I've ever tried to do is get you on that list."

I understand perfectly his reluctance to admit to it, but I cannot be party to it. I wander out into the corridor to gather my strength.

On my return, he is triumphant.

"That doctor popped his head back in to see me and he reckons I'm right and that I don't need to go on the list just yet."

He is greatly cheered at this. I say nothing but my instinct tells me that this is the wrong decision and the assessment team agree with me. They are due to have a meeting this afternoon, to assess and place in order of need all their patients. We will know the outcome after they have come to a decision.

The tension is ticking away like a time bomb. We sit staring at the wall opposite, willing the clock round to three-thirty, the most likely time for the ward round.

Then suddenly, they are here, surrounding the bed.

"We have some news," the co-ordinator announces, with a wide smile. "We've decided you are now a suitable candidate for transplant. We're putting you on the list as soon as possible."

Jim nods warily as he thanks them. I say nothing. Not even, 'I told you so.' For once, I am too numb to speak.

A week later, we are squeezed into a tiny broom cupboard of an office at Southampton General Hospital with the peripatetic team from Addenbrooke's hospital. This would be comical if it wasn't so serious, space being at a premium.

"I should have brought some nibbles," jokes the doctor. "We could have made a party of it."

Everyone grins, keen to dispel any tension. They know how overwhelming an experience this can be for a patient. Then they begin their brief introduction.

"This is Angela, transplant co-ordinator. This is Dr Davis, he's the anaesthetist. Then there's..."

Around the room we go, nodding, smiling and shaking nine hands. The upshot is that they are hoping to get Jim up to Cambridge very shortly. Sooner would be better, they assure us.

"How do you feel about that, Jim?" Angela asks.

"Well," he takes a deep breath. "Obviously I'm a bit nervous."

She nods in sympathy.

"But," he continues, "it's my only chance now, really, isn't it? Plus the wife has been nagging me non stop about it for months."

"I'm the wife," I announce, drily.

The team chuckle.

"It's only because I love you so much, you do know that, don't you?" I tell him afterwards.

"Course." He looks briefly embarrassed and a bit teary. It does that to you, all of this. It's a lot to take in.

I can't get my head around the fact that by the time Jim gets called up, someone who is alive and well now will have died and as a result Jim can live.

"It's just so sad." I burst into tears.

"Oh, Kerry. I know. I feel awful about it all." He is weepy too now.

I straighten up immediately. "I'm so sorry. You don't need me being a stupid idiot at a time like this. I'm just scared, Jim. I love you so much. I don't know what I'd do…"

He knows exactly what I am saying.

"You? You'll get snapped up," he insists.

"I wouldn't want to. It's you I love," I counter immediately.

I pause as curiosity impels me to ask. "What would you do, Jim? If I went first?"

"I wouldn't marry anyone else," he says decisively.

"But I would want you to." I am upset at the thought of him being unhappy without me. "What about Joanna Lumley?"

He thinks for a moment. "Well, maybe for Joanna." He grins at me, slyly, with a glint in his eye.

"She's a bit wrinkly." I screw up my nose, dismissing the competition. But insecurity rankles in me. "Would you really?"

"Don't be daft. Where would I find another one like you, dinlow?"

I think for a moment. "You wouldn't find anyone to burn your dinners like I can."

"Very true. Now let that be an end to your nonsense."

We watch Larry Sanders and get to laughing instead. Burying your head in the sand is not only therapeutic, sometimes it's the only course available to you.

CHAPTER 62

The call comes on 24 September 2007. Jim, shaking with relief, puts the phone down and immediately rings me at work.

"Oh, my God! That's wonderful!"

Unable to concentrate, I leave work early and race to catch the next train home.

I throw my arms around him at the station, but he is curiously subdued.

We celebrate with coffee in a nearby pub that was once the local Registry Office. Years ago, my mother and father tied the knot here. They had their picture taken outside, in black and white.

"How are you feeling, I mean really?"

"I feel nervous," he admits.

I take his hand and we fall silent. I open the plastic lid of the cream and pour it into my coffee, stirring longer than necessary, lost in thought, trying to remember what life was like before the threat of death took over.

"We'll get you through this, Jim, I promise. I will be with you every step of the way. We are doing this together, remember. Team McPhail."

I am the cheerleader, the chief coach and bottle-washer. I spur him on to believe in himself, but his reaction to the news is surprisingly muted. I had expected this moment to change everything. Now I realise that getting on to the list is no assurance of actually receiving a transplant in time. Getting a transplant is no assurance of surviving a transplant either. There is no end to this road. Jim, of course, knows this. He is better acquainted with the realistic chances of his survival than I am willing to be. Right now, I would beg, borrow or steal to get my hands on a bit of hope, even while Jim is learning the graceful art of surrender and acceptance. Of the two of us, he is the wiser.

Sleep is hard to come by for both of us. We are in a permanent state of alertness, waiting for the telephone to ring, day or night. Jim's skin is perpetually itching now because of the increased levels of bilirubin in his bloodstream. He tosses and turns and scratches in bed. I groan and urge him to settle down. He gets up and pads about the flat, not wanting to disturb me.

"Can't you just lie down and be quiet?" I rant, impatient and crazy with insomnia. Be careful what you wish for, my conscience chides me. I shut my eyes and curse the disease to hell for what it has done to him.

Every moment together is imbued with intense meaning. We are rich beyond our wildest dreams with our appreciation of one another. At work, he winks at me across the desk and I blush, smiling to myself because I know that he is thinking of me. If I leave work after him, he wanders round the shops, then comes to meet me at the station. It is always exciting to see him again. Never once in our time together has the thrill of being with him been lost. My knees still buckle when I catch sight of him.

Our horizons shrink as life gets focused on survival. Once, we dreamt of seeing Rome. Now we do as the Romans do and on sunny days sit outdoors at pavement cafes, drinking in our ridiculous good fortune at having found each other.

As Autumn approaches, the nights draw in. Darker days are ahead and there is nothing we can do to prevent them. Now we are washed up on the desert island of our bed, with our precious books and favourite films – the only treasures that survived the wreckage. We have given up all thoughts of rescue. The telephone seldom rings and when it does, it is never the hospital. We have both drawn up wills.

Signing them was undeniably awful, like being forced into a pact with your own mortality. We hide them in a box. I know that the next time I look at them, he will already be lost to me.

Still we maintain the façade that all is normal. A jolly tide of friends and family refuse to acknowledge the truth that Jim is dying. His face is grey now, with the effort of keeping going. His eyes, too large, too dark in his head, shadowed with circles, plead silently for release.

In the early hours of Tuesday morning, the telephone rings.

"Oh, my God! Jim, this is it!"

I dive out of bed, shaking, to take the call. If it is Addenbrooke's, we have merely hours to make the trip to the emergency room at Cambridge while they await the arrival of Jim's donor organ.

"Wrong number!" I burst into tears, then return to Jim's side, both of us bitterly disappointed.

This is how it will be. Whenever Jim's mobile ring tone sounds, whenever our landline rings…

But the call eludes us. We have been on twenty-four hour call up for two full months now. Friends discreetly avoid calling us, anxious not to cause us further pain, or interrupt an expected call.

Every other week we attend the hospital. We sit in the waiting room. Jim can't make the journey here now without it utterly exhausting him.

The team are as professional as ever. But I detect their own anxiety beneath the scripted reassurance and am horrified. Finally, the doctor admits the truth.

"I'm afraid we're facing a dire situation at the moment due to severe shortages in donations of organs. The media coverage has hardly helped the situation. We used to do eight operations a month but we're down to three at the moment, if we're lucky."

They are, in fact, so desperate to save lives that they recently transplanted a liver from an eighty year old donor. The recipient died shortly afterwards. They had no choice. Without it he would have died anyway.

"We'll see you again in two weeks. If you haven't already received your call up by then, of course."

We shake hands with the doctor for the last time. Thankfully, we are unaware of the fact.

"I think, you know, these things happen for a reason. I'm convinced of it," I tell Jim with false brightness. "It's often when things seem at their most impossible that miraculous things happen. Maybe because of the donor situation, you'll prove to be a match when others aren't and jump up the list or something?"

He squeezes my hand. "Exactly."

We go off and try to enjoy the afternoon. We explore the fantastic natural history museum and round it off with a river walk. But we can't settle. There is too much weighing on us. Too much at stake.

His bravery is tremendous but I can't match it. I am losing him, hour by hour, and I cannot bear it.

CHAPTER 63

It is October. I watch him as he walks back across the common, waving to me. He is incredibly beautiful. I can no longer put into words the depths of my feelings for him. It is a song my soul knows. I blink back tears. It is a wonderful, glorious feeling, this love for another human being. But he is dying. My time with him is slipping slowly through my fingers, like so many grains of sand, and it is impossible to hold on to him because he is not mine to keep. When time summons him, he will leave me.

We sit together in the park at lunchtime. Lazy butterflies and drunken wasps career around a carousel of flowers. Yellow, gold and fiery red leaves fall gently to the ground around us. They will never again grace this tree with their presence. The leaves that emerge next year will be different, if no less beautiful. It is a hard truth to absorb. I am not sure I can. Nothing will replace what has been lost. Not the entire roll call of the universe itself. For it will not be him the spring urges forth.

Behind the scenes Jim is expressing anxiety. Friends report back that he is worried about how I shall manage in the months ahead. Poor love, that he should even concern himself with me when he is in the very depths of suffering himself.

"You have to get the transplant, Jim, and you have to get well. You do understand that there is no other way, now?"

Our friend Kay is desperate for Jim to acknowledge this. He nods, but looks away, out of the window. She is puzzled. It is not like him to be evasive.

I never give him the luxury of doubt. There is no room for failure. The doctors will not contemplate it and neither will I. Having made it this far, we are going to succeed in keeping Jim alive. I cannot exist on a knife edge of what ifs. What ifs will not save him.

The words of his consultant are ringing in my ears.

"I'm afraid even with a transplant, there is the probability of the hepatitis C returning at some point. Of course we can begin treatment earlier this time…"

We have ended up in a blind alley. Rapidly, one by one, the exits are closing off. Jim and I dodge the Grim Reaper in one corridor, only to be confronted by him in the next.

I want never to be party to it again, this song of the seasons that cripples my heart. There is a chill in the air.

Dare we risk a last trip to London? What if we receive the call up to Addenbrooke's en route?

"Ach, well, if we do, we're halfway up to Cambridge at least," Jim decides.

We challenge death with our lack of deference and refuse to be cowed by its threats.

*

And yet now, as we travel to London, we both know in our hearts that the telephone call will never come. We don't say it out loud. Not yet.

Morning fields, painted in sunlight, sail past the window. The journey is forever imprinted on me. Deer poised in the distance, silhouetted between autumnal trees, raise their heads. How will they look to me when he is gone? Will their beauty only magnify the loss? I study Jim intently while he reads his paper opposite me. He looks up and winks as if to acknowledge that he knows, but let's just enjoy today.

We rejoice in our old haunts. Trawling around Borough Market with its noisy, industrious market holders. It is alive with colour. The fish stall, with its marble slabs, is resplendent with crabs and mussels, lobsters and monkfish. A cornucopia of the ocean. The air is filled with laughter and wine as bartering Frenchmen display loaves of all sizes in vast woven baskets. Bunting flutters above their heads and the sky is azure blue. A mouse scoots beneath the stalls, head down, urgently seeking crumbs, and no one sees him but me.

We drink hot coffee in takeaway cups from a pavement kiosk, enjoying the afternoon crowds who have assembled to drink and chatter outside the pub. We explore the hidden alleyways that criss cross the back of the market. It is Friday, the best day of the week.

By the butcher's stall, the trader is crouching low. He has his apron on and a wooden mallet in his hand. Suddenly, at his feet, I see the bloodied broken body of the mouse. I turn away, upset. Jim too is shaken. All life is precious to us.

We retire to the grounds of Southwark Cathedral and sit together. Opposite us, on one of the wooden benches is an exhausted kitchen worker, curled up asleep in his overalls, shoes neatly parked beneath him. Jim takes a stealthy photo, then goes and poses behind a stone sculpture, his head poking mischievously out from the top, grinning like a boy, while I snap his picture. He enjoys making me laugh.

Back in the market, we spy a camera crew filming behind a wire enclosure. A runner with a clipboard spots us and races over, brimming with enthusiasm.

"Excuse me, we're looking for members of the public to take part in a TV show. Would you like to join us?"

I squeeze Jim's hand and we grin. "Go on then!"

We are escorted on to the film set. Jim is flagged by two glamorous female presenters while I share a joke with the fierce-looking cameraman who sports a purple Mohican. I sit at the makeshift table in the camera tent, and watch Jim with utter astonishment.

"Fancy you being on TV!" I tease him. "You were amazing. I watched it all from the camera."

Afterwards, they discover Jim is waiting for a liver transplant. Arms around him, the programme presenters pose with him for a photograph.

"Thank you so much," I beam at them.

"This is the most fun I've had in ages," confides the cameraman with the chains hanging down from his ears and a spike through his nose. He laughs and whispers in my ear, "I'm actually the make-up artist, but we were short-handed today, so I got to have a go at this instead!" He sweeps off into the distance, boom in hand, a grin still plastered to his face.

They will let us know the dates for screening. Our last ever trip to London and we made it onto national TV. Who would have thought?

As for the rest of it, I don't think I can bear to watch any more. It's happening in close up now. That's the trouble with reality. It exposes you to too much truth.

CHAPTER 64

Winter is coming on fast. An icy cold wind licks our faces as we cross the footbridge where tiny blue lights sparkle in the tree branches after dark. In the distance a tall ship is moored at the entrance to the harbour, its mast reaching up towards the stars.

Not long now. I squeeze his hand in hope. It is Friday night. The call could still come at any time. We swing like a pendulum between hope and defeat.

In the restaurant, he puts his mobile phone on the table, just to be sure we hear it. A simple act of faith. He is in surprisingly good spirits, even though he is tired. We sparkle together. Like the first time. Just like it's always been between us.

Afterwards we stride along, hand in hand, daring the cold to come near us.

"Let's play rock paper scissors."

"OK, but make it interesting... we'll just do it in our heads."

"You first!"

I study his face intently. He smiles, knowingly.

"Rock!" I suggest.

"Yes!" He grins, and turns to watch me.

"Scissors!"

"How did you know?" I ask.

We take turns, laughing. No miming with hands. No props. We have perfected the easy telepathy of long-term lovers.

"I am so happy right now!" I beam at him.

He is serenely confident. "Good." He pulls me towards him and

JAMES WITH A SILENT C

kisses me. A wonderful peace encompasses us both. We are facing the biggest battle of our lives. Waiting for the call that has the power to change everything. I sense that beneath the surface things are moving rapidly, are changing. Things over which we were, perhaps, never in control.

"I've already had a bath tonight!" Jim insists.

"You're a liar!" I declare. "Now get in that bathroom before I take my boot to your behind!"

He beams like a naughty child. He had no intention of going anywhere near the bathtub.

"It's no good lying to me, Jim McPhail," I laugh, "because I always know when you are. You remember that!"

I love him. I adore him. I am swollen with pride over him, my beautiful man. I can't resist pushing the door open and peeking at him.

"Go away! It's freezing!" He objects, closely followed by, "Can you come and fetch me a towel, my love?" on realising he cannot reach from bath to rail.

I watch him clamber out, his gorgeous chest with its dark hair, his huge eyelashes framing his manly face. His arms and legs are powerfully built. You would hardly stop him in the street and pick an argument with him.

"A man stopped me once and asked me, "If you could be God for one day, what would you do?""

"Aha. And what did you tell him, my love?"

"I said that I would make myself God permanently."

"And what did he say?"

"He said no one could do that."

"And."

"I said, if I was God I could do whatever I liked." Jim reveals the feelings of irritation he felt at the time. He puts on his night things and marches out of the bathroom, feeling satisfied with himself.

He was right.

In the night I watch him sleeping. His breath rises and falls rhythmically. I try to synchronise my breath to his breaths but they are too shallow and fast now compared with my deeper, measured ones.

He is awake now. Early dawn. He pulls me to him and kisses me and we make love again. His eyes are sensitive, watchful. I cup the back of his head with my hands. I long to keep him safe. I am so afraid of having to let him go.

"We should go out for the day," he announces over coffee.

"But you're too tired," I object.

He shakes his head. "I want to go, while we still have the chance."

He means before the call comes, doesn't he?

Nearly Christmas. The decorations and lights that dance above the High Street in Chichester were surely laid on in celebration of our arrival? We spend the afternoon in the Army and Navy Store, overlooking the cathedral, tucked in a cosy corner with tea and buns. St Richard's stature draws a dramatic figure in the darkness, raising his hand to make the sign on the cross. These are the crisp clear nights of years ago when my father and I would set out in search of monsters in the dark. Now I hope never to find them again.

Jim sleeps on the train home, head bent low, as if in prayer, arms folded in resignation at his fate. I want to drink in every moment with him. If he knew the true depth of my love for him, he would be devastated at the thought of ever leaving me.

Friends appear on the doorstep when we get home. Jim is exhausted but valiantly props himself in the chair to be sociable. Even now. Eventually I chase them off, brusque but smiling. Putting my ailing man to bed, he shivers slightly and I draw protectively around him.

Let me step back in time. I want to gather Jim safely up and keep him tight against my heart where the passage of time cannot ruin us.

In the end, you see, we must give everything up. Not just home, not just possessions, but everything and everyone you have ever loved. That is the nature of the crucifixion, that is the power of the resurrection, right there in that centre of pain.

CHAPTER 65

Jim is not well at all this morning. Aching and shivering, he objects to me coaxing him to take the day off work, and is gone and on the train before I can prevent him. Hours later, grey and pale, he returns home. By then, I am at work. He phones me to tell me he is all right. "It's just flu, honestly, nothing for you to worry about."

Nothing to worry about, except that by the time I return home, he cannot manage to eat and can barely drink.

"Will you try a cup of tea, at least?" I ask, hollow with concern.

He nods. "I'm sorry."

"Oh, don't be," I remonstrate, throwing my arms around his shoulders. He is boiling hot, in spite of the cold grey November chill that hangs like a wolf about the door, drawing ever nearer and threatening to ruin everything.

Death has no business creeping so close to him.

He falls asleep again and I slip into bed beside him.

"Good night, sweetheart." He stirs and murmurs.

"Good night, my love. You just wake me up if you need me at all. Promise."

He is restless in the night. Does he know that the end is approaching? Is that why he cannot settle?

"Please try to sleep, Jim," I beg. I am exhausted from weeks without proper rest.

"Sorry," he mouths, but he is being driven to distraction by the perpetual itching.

Nothing but a transplant operation can save him now. Every night

I lie awake, willing the call to come. Every morning I rise and it has not. In cruel perpetuity, the days follow on, one from another, offering hope then snatching it back from under us.

One night, after he has staggered to the bathroom, he returns dazed and disoriented. This is encephalopathy setting in. I am terrified of what lies ahead of him now.

"Oh, Jim! Please just settle down, would you?" I yell at him, hurling the bed clothes clean off the bed, driven nearly insane with lack of sleep, knowing that in three hours from now, I have to get up and repeat the endless treadmill of work. I am so close to a breakdown that I can barely function.

When he slips back into bed, he is weeping. I am beyond cruel. Clinging to the life raft of my own survival, I am unwilling to even comfort him.

"I'm so sorry," he whispers. "Please believe me."

My heart stings with shame that I can behave so badly towards him. This is the man I love with all my heart. Am I losing my own sanity?

The next morning I ring work.

"I won't be in today. Jim is not well."

I race into town to buy a few essentials, then dive back to be with him, hardly daring to leave him alone.

I return and make a fresh bed up while he stands shivering to one side. Then he creeps back under the warmth of the covers. I pat him in, gently tucking the sheets around him, maternal and apologetic.

"I'm so so sorry, love. It was the last thing you deserved, me going on at you in the night."

My brave soldier, my little sparrow, close to dying now.

Nothing to do but wait, wait for the call. I climb in beside him, out of the cold and sit up, reading while he sleeps.

It must pass, surely, this virus? He aches still and now his tummy is swelling up. In the night he is awake again and agitated. He pulls down the sheet, clutching his tummy.

"That's it. I'm ringing the hospital." I leap out of bed.

"Don't you dare do that! I don't want you to!" He shouts.

"Jim, this is ridiculous! You're not well. I'm ringing the doctor at least."

He glowers, adamant he does not want me to, but he is contorted in pain.

Shaking with fear and with trembling fingers, I dial the emergency number.

Minutes later the emergency doctor is with us. Jim needs to go straight into hospital. We ring the transplant team at Addenbrooke's. In view of his condition, they opt to have him taken to A&E at Southampton General, rather than risk a longer journey.

CHAPTER 66

The doctors will not tell Jim that he is dying.

"He hasn't asked me outright, but I think he knows," his consultant whispers to me, out of earshot.

Jim has been dying ever since he was admitted to Intensive Care five days ago but this is the first time that the medical profession has actually confirmed it. I have to know. And I don't want Jim to hear. We are making a mockery of the situation, the doctors and I. None of us can bear to speak the truth.

"He's tired of being prodded and poked around," the consultant says.

This is an understatement of the worst kind. Jim has been to hell and back over the course of his disease.

"Should we tell him?"

"Hard to say. We mustn't lie to him. If he asks me outright, I will be forced to tell him. But I don't want to steal what little hope is left."

I turn and walk towards my husband whose arms are stretched out towards me. He grabs me in a bear hug. He does know, I can tell. What's worse is that he now knows that I have been told. I cannot forgive myself for welling up. Tears invade my eyes like needles, but I force them to retreat inward. I refuse to cry openly in front of him. I will not dignify this huge and terrible secret by acknowledging it openly.

"This is the best thing that could have happened because last time we didn't get this chance," he whispers. I cannot stand his bravery.

The medical professionals surround us like an armed guard. We are unwilling captives, both of us.

"Always remember how much I love you," he continues.

I pull away just enough to gaze into his large soulful eyes. His beautiful black lashes would grace any woman but on his sturdy stoic features they lend him an air of beautiful vulnerability.

"Look at you!" I marvel. "You're brilliant!" Best thing I ever did was marry you!"

"You're brilliant," he insists.

But he is quite wrong. I cannot think about any pain but my own. I cannot summon up the deep compassion he is able to show me. To my eternal shame, it is weeks before I truly contemplate what those final conscious moments must have been like for him.

There is a strong hand on my shoulder. A deep reassuring voice in my ear.

"We are going to do everything we possibly can to make him comfortable." The anaesthetist is at Jim's side. The kindness of this big, burly man inspires hope when all is lost.

"Thank you."

I walk slowly away. As I turn, I am just in time to see Jim lift his oxygen mask and turn to speak briefly to one of the nurses.

I cannot see down the corridor that leads to the waiting room. My eyes are blurred from crying. I sink down onto a chair, oblivious to my surroundings, and wait.

*

At 4 o'clock that afternoon I met with the medical team and gave them my consent to turn off Jim's life support machine.

Now we are back in the isolation room in Intensive Care. Jim is no longer conscious. He is lying prostrate on the bed. The nurse, a young girl in her early twenties, has expertly removed the banks of computer equipment in my absence. There will be no more catheters or intravenous drips. No more ventilators or Ng tubes. Jim is free at last of the constraints between himself and mortality.

I take his big warm hand in my own and although he cannot see me, and I think he cannot hear me, I sit and talk to him as if this were any ordinary Tuesday. His eyes are open but glazed over with medical gel to prevent their drying. He looks beautiful to me. His sufferings only ever added to his greatness.

"He's always been such a brave man," I tell the nurse. "I just don't want him suffering any longer."

I say this aloud, because I want it to be true. But I do not want Jim to die. I do not want to be left alone in this world without him.

"Just before he was sedated, he took off his oxygen mask and said, "I just want to thank you all for all the help you've given me," she tells me, tears pricking her own eyes. She sets about making me comfortable. I have a soft chair, a cup of freshly brewed tea.

"I can stay with you, or if you would prefer to be alone, I can be just outside the door?"

I want to be alone with Jim. She understands perfectly.

"If you need me, I'll just be the other side of the glass."

She is kindness itself. The blinds are drawn down over the window and the door. She departs and Jim and I are alone together at last.

I gaze up at the large clock on the wall every so often. Five o'clock becomes six o'clock. When I can no longer bear to talk without crying, I sing softly to him. Bob Dylan's *Blind Willie McTell*. I like Joan Baez too. She was in love with Dylan once. But Dylan did not return her intensity. I sing *Sweet Sir Galahad*, mouthing the words self-consciously.

Jim will never again put his arms around me. Not this side of earth. I curl up and place my head on the pillow beside his. I cannot bear to be here, but there is nowhere else I would want to be at this moment. God is faithful. I prayed so hard that I would be here for Jim when the time came, that I would not miss the opportunity to say goodbye.

Jim does love me, really love me. I am the luckiest woman in the world. I love him so much, love the very bones of him. I would lay

JAMES WITH A SILENT C

down my own life for him in an instant if I could. I want to lie beside him forever and feel his soft gentle breath on my face as he exhales. But we do not have forever. We have at best tonight. Maybe not even that long. No one has said how long it will be. No one knows with any certainty. A great wall of pretence that was built around us since Jim's admission is being dismantled brick by brick. Doctors have entered and exited, skilfully dodging with consummate ease my inevitable question. Nurses have come and gone, weaving hopelessly optimistic predictions. Jim's own team from hepatology arrived today at 3 p.m. one hour before his life support was switched off. They made confident predictions regarding the transplant team at Addenbrooke's. I let them. His favourite nurse was off today, but had promised to visit him tomorrow. I am glad she will not see Jim die. That she will hear of his death only after it has been translated into paperwork and he has become another statistic. She will remember only the living breathing Jim who made her laugh, always had a ready smile for her and enjoyed being made a fuss of.

Around six o'clock, I cannot endure any more. I get up. I whisper reassuringly to Jim that I will be back soon and leave the room. Instinct tells me I must get out because it feels as if the very walls of the room are about to close in on us.

I sit downstairs, completely numb, and drink an over-sweet cup of coffee from the machines that line that walls of the canteen. Days before, a doctor came in search of me here, to update me on Jim's condition. Now there will be no more updates.

I return upstairs. Out in the corridor, I sink down onto a ledge by a window box of artificial flowers. I grab my mobile phone from my handbag and ring my best friend. "I can't do this. I really can't. It's too hard!" I sob. Just then, my hand touches something in the flower bed. I draw my fingers around it. When I open my hand, a red admiral butterfly nestles in it. Lifeless but perfectly beautiful.

"Oh my God! That's really strange! I've just put my hand down among the flowers here and now there's a butterfly in my hand, just like the one Jim and I saw in the tower at Canterbury!" I am talking to myself. It would not make sense to anyone else. But I remember vividly the first year after my mother's death, when Jim took me to Canterbury. When the red admiral had fluttered up from the floorboards on that bitterly cold day in the Westgate tower, I had known that my mother's spirit was still alive.

I carry the butterfly with me and gently lay it on top of the intercom when I buzz to request re-admittance to Intensive Care. The beautiful coincidence has given me the strength I need to go on.

Back in the room, I sense the dawn of the faintest beginning of peace. The walls are no longer restrictive. We are not in darkness. Jim continues to breath softly, courtesy of a little white pipe in his mouth.

Three more hours pass. The clock ticks on and Jim continues to exist.

Then, towards ten o'clock, I sense a change in him. Time has become less of an endurance test for us both. Something infinitely more precious is apparent.

I feel Jim's awareness change. Without knowing what it is, I sense a light or flickering on the opposite side of the bed to where I am sitting. A presence, indescribable, comes close alongside Jim. I feel Jim's interest quicken as if he is keenly aware of something or someone at his right hand side. A childlike sense of excitement is on his countenance. I squeeze his hand and almost before I know it, the words are out of my mouth.

"It's all right, lovey. I do know. You just go whenever you're ready. Go and see your dad and Arthur and your mum and all your friends."

At that very instant he passes over. I see a tiny, brilliant light leave his body and vanish into a swirling circle of light which I know to be the presence that had been by his bed. A huge wave of elation engulfs me. The exact opposite of the crippling shock I had expected. This,

I know now, is the perfect fulfilment of my purpose in Jim's life. The tears I had fought back, sixteen years before, when I barely knew him suddenly equate perfectly with this moment. The tragedy, always foreseen, has been swept from under him in a rare triumph.

"Oh, Jim! You are fantastic! I knew you could do it!"

How strange my words seem to me now, after his death. Perhaps I meant only that Jim was wonderful in allowing me to be present as he passed over. Joy overtook us both at the moment of absolute crisis and Jim, I am certain, had wanted me to experience it as clearly as he had.

It was raining outside the hospital entrance. Not the wild, frenzied rain that had made the last few days so torturous, but a gentle, misty rain. The car park was floodlit in the distance. I walked up the concourse and gently placed the butterfly on a hedge, then walked slowly back towards the hospital. It was done. It was over. Never again would Jim suffer.

When I returned to him, I held his hand for as long as I could, committing him to memory. Then I put my arms around his dear, gentle frame one last time and said goodbye before walking out of the ward forever.

CHAPTER 67

I thought it would end here. Everything came to a halt that winter. The ground froze over and the dead flowers, long fallen to the ground, were in their final resting place in the earth.

The rains were unceasing and the gales blew, as if, apart from the one clear day of his funeral, the weather too would mourn his absence forever.

The reappearance of the sun startled me. It took months for me even to notice it. To see that the blossoms had reappeared on the branches and to hear the wren bursting into song outside my window.

In the midst of my grief, I lost all contact with the world. My husband was dead. My mother, to whom I might naturally have gravitated for comfort, was also gone. My father was still grieving. Like a woman drowning, I grasped the hands offered by friends, but they could not always hold on to me for as long as I needed them to. The intensity of my grief was frightening, both to them and to me.

One Sunday in July, I sank down on a park bench, at my bleakest, blackest point. Nothing, not even the blisteringly hot sun could penetrate the darkness that was consuming me. I was utterly exhausted. My very bones ached with the effort of continuing without him.

I made my decision. I had sufficient quantities of tablets stored up. Floating down the road home, it was as though I no longer existed. Only pain was tethering me to reality.

Establishing the dosage, determined to succeed, I began to write a letter, composed and calm, explaining it was nobody's fault but my own.

At the time, I was dangerously numb, beyond help or expression. I did not know how stupid and selfish a gesture I was contemplating. Then it hit me. I saw, in my mind's eye, a stretcher leaving my home for the last time. An ambulance, just like the one that had arrived for Jim, would be tearing away into the distance. I saw myself placed on the liver transplant list. Just like Jim. I imagined my life being saved. Unlike Jim. Had I gone ahead, and survived, I would have had to live every day with the guilt and shame of how I had sullied his memory.

I hurled the tablets into the kitchen bin. I threw myself onto the bed. Lying where he used to lay, I cried and cried until I was physically beyond expression of my pain. Rising up at last, I vowed that I would carry on until my own days ended. If the pain never shifted, no matter. I would find a way to go on. In the height of my grief, I saw only one possible meaning in all this. My task was to carry the pain of our parting so that Jim did not have to. It was the least I could do for him.

The next day my father came to meet me and we went for a walk. I was so adept at hiding how bleak I was feeling that I did not bat an eyelid as we strolled across the park.

"I used to play football here as a child," my father exclaimed, delightedly. I winced at the revelation, picturing a skinny, dark haired boy running to kick a ball, laughing with his friends, long ago. I saw Jim and me holding hands, with our lives ahead of us. People don't want to confront their own mortality. It is too terrifying a prospect, especially for those who have no faith. I am luckier than most. I do have faith. Those who know me best see the certainty of it in me. Others, no doubt, think me weak, clinging to branches purely because I was drowning. They are wrong. I was dragged kicking and screaming back to God. He wasn't my choice. He chose me. How I long for that safe corner of my former life where, with my back against the wall, I could pretend that I was still in charge of it all. But it's only ever in the centre of our pain that we truly know Him. That is the true nature of the crucifixion and it is ultimately our redemption because without it, we would never develop real compassion towards one another.

How do I know there is more? I know, because without my faith I would have ended it on that hot July day but something whispered to me and told me to hold on.

It was the same voice Jim had heard all those years before. I recognised it. In the end, you see, his story saved my own.

Love will always remain between us. Death should be ashamed of itself for thinking it could ever steal him from me.

Our stories hold us together. A link of human hands across the years. Those stories call to us to remember, even as they urge us onwards, trusting us to pass the memories on up the line. Love can never be broken. It binds us together even as it, ultimately, sets us free. It's what we came here to discover, travellers all.

For a long time I was haunted by his pain. I would hear him calling out to me in the night in desperation. I would watch from the lounge window, waiting for him to come striding up the road. Walking up the stairs at work, I remembered only too well his laboured breathing and his exhausted expression.

But love is not a study in chronology. It is not satisfied by time. It is beautiful and enduring and spectacular and intricate. It is a snowflake, melting on the tongue, a work of art. It requires dedication and honesty. It never costs less than everything. It is always worth it.

In Glasgow, I set his ashes down at last, alongside the memorial to his mother and father. A butterfly alights briefly on the oak tree beside his final resting place. Another joins it and they dance briefly and joyously in a circle of eight above the flowers. As I kneel to watch them, the sun on my back, I am reminded that life goes on.

I walk the streets, searching for him, until at last I come to Jamaica Street, close to the bridge and stand, talking with his sister Beth. I see suddenly that he is everywhere. The excitable boy astride his beloved father's motorbike, the eager child clambering up the steps of Wilson's Zoo, bucket of bread in hand to feed the lion, the lost adolescent adrift in the park, gazing dreamily out at an unseen future, the heroin addict, lying slumped against the wall of a squalid flat, hopeless and alone, the beaming bridegroom, eyes shining with pride as he takes his vows, the man whose courage and compassion amazed everyone as he fought for his life. They are all present in a cacophony of voices that lift and float away on the air.

A year to the day he died, I have a waking vision of him. He is skating around the edge of a lake with his hands tucked behind his back. He is wearing his black coat and his dark blue scarf, the one I bought him two Christmasses ago. He does not spot me at first, but then he catches sight of me. He skates to the centre of the lake and holds his arms wide open, inviting me towards him. I long to go to him. But I know, instinctively, that the second I step onto the ice, it will crack underfoot and send him plummeting into the dark depths. Worse still, I know he is aware of this, but for my sake is willing to take that terrible risk.

It is then that I know I love him too much to take that chance. If I am strong enough to wait and endure, one day the ice will thicken and I will cross safely to him. He understands perfectly.

As a child, I loved the story of the Snow Queen. Of the demon mirror, carried up to heaven that grinned and shook and splintered into a million pieces. Fragments lodged themselves in Kay's heart and eyes, blinding him to all that was good and lovely in the world. The Snow Queen held him captive in her palace and only his true love, Gerda, could ever hope to save him.

On the final page of the story, they are reunited and swirl around in each other's arms laughing with joy as they skate together on the ice. They turn to discover that all the splinters of the mirror that had been dancing alongside them have settled on the surface to spell out the letters of a single word. It is the word that Kay has been searching for all along.

It is eternity.